CU00641623

KOI
MEDICINE

British Library Cataloguing in Publication Data
A CIP record for this book is available from the British Library

ISBN 1 85279 177 2

Published by Kingdom Books PO9 5TL England.

KOI
MEDICINE

LANCE JEPSON
MA VetMB CBiol MIBiol MRCVS

This book is dedicated to my parents, Edna and Gordon, without whom this book would have been a biological impossibility. They unwittingly started me on a lifetime fascination with fish and gave me the emotional and financial backing to fulfil my ambitions.

I also dedicate this book to my partner and colleague Lisa, for her helpful comments on radiography and for enduring the result of my lifetime fascination.

Finally to my sons, Charlton, Quaid and Lloyd – may they find the same wonder and pleasure in Nature as I have always found.

Contents

Introduction

The keeping of koi (*Cyprinus carpio var.*) is an extremely popular hobby throughout the world. This book is designed to be a starting point for veterinary surgeons, professional fish health practitioners and advanced hobbyists into the field of koi health. Certain concepts potentially new to the veterinary surgeon, such as water quality, together with some areas not normally considered in other books are discussed in detail. In the main however, I have tried to concentrate on the most important aspects of cause, diagnosis and treatment.

Chapter One
Water Quality

The most important part of koi husbandry and health management is the concept of water quality – the term that covers all thermal, physical and chemical parameters of water.

1.1.1 Temperature
Thermal properties of water are:-

a) High specific heat capacity so it resists temperature changes. Any temperature changes in nature are relatively slow, so as a general rule fish have not evolved to cope with rapid temperature fluctuations.
b) Water is at its most dense at 4°C. If ponds are deep enough with limited water currents then stratification of the water layers occurs, with the bottom layer at 4°C (the hypolimnion) and colder or warmer water above this (epilimnion). This is known as a thermocline and is important because it provides a relatively warm area for the dormant fish to sit out the winter. Conversely in tropical climates the hypolimnion will provide a cool area. Since the hypolimnion mixes very poorly with the overlying water layer, it can become deoxygenated and shunned by koi, so very deep pools serve no function as the koi may not utilise the full depth. Even in relatively shallow ponds, a degree of stratification occurs, unless water currents are instigated to prevent this.

1.1.2 Koi are ectotherms
That is to say they rely upon external heat sources to drive their metabolism, as distinct from endotherms such as mammals which produce a significant amount of heat from their normal biochemical reactions.

However fish are generally perceived to be thermoconformers, their body temperature being the same as, and varying in parallel with, the ambient water temperature. Koi are regarded in the hobby as "coldwater" and as such are expected to tolerate temperatures from just above freezing to mid thirties centigrade. In aquaculture however, they are referred to as "warmwater" – indeed the Preferred Body Temperature (PBT) of carp lies between 22-28°C which means that given the opportunity koi are thermoregulators, not thermoconformers. The PBT of an ectotherm can be regarded as the body temperature that animal strives to maintain by behavioural and physiological means. This usually coincides with the optimum temperature for its metabolic processes such as digestion, muscle activity and immunity. In its simplest form this would involve our hypothetical carp moving along a temperature gradient until it reached water with a range of 22-28°C.

Silver carp (*Hypopthalmichthys molitrix*), a related cyprinid, exhibit diurnal movement patterns in ponds that allow them to thermoregulate. Colour may prove important. Wild carp are darker on the dorsal surface to help disguise them from aerial predators. However dark surfaces are better absorbers of radiation therefore these fish may well heat up more quickly than lighter coloured fish when exposed to sunlight in shallow waters. This may be part of the reason why some of the faster growing varieties of koi tend to be darker coloured.

1.1.3 Temperature adaptation

A 10°C change in water temperature will produce a two fold change in metabolic rate (Q10 =2). Carp have a preferred body temperature of 22-28°C, and although a range of 16-28°C is usually considered adequate for koi and goldfish, they can acclimate to temperatures outside that range if gradually adjusted. Goldfish have an upper lethal temperature of 40°C, with lower lethal temperatures of 10°C, 5°C or 1°C if acclimated to 35°C, 25°C and 15°C respectively. Temperature changes within a natural body of water are usually only 3-4°C over a 24 hour period. Overall seasonal changes can be greater but the longer timecourse allows for a period of adaptation.

Below 15°C metabolism is limited by temperature, whereas above this the main constraint is oxygen concentration. Theoretically it is possible that energy liberation at low temperatures may not be sufficient to support life. However cold-adapted muscle has an increased number of mitochondria and there is an increased activity in certain enzymes, possibly by switching between iso-enzymes with different thermal properties, or turning to alternative metabolic pathways.

Further cold adaptations include modifications to the nervous system. The temperature tolerance of goldfish can be extended by the addition of cholesterol or phospholipids to their diet, possibly due to alterations in the neuronal cell membranes.

In both goldfish and carp there is a reduction in the number of red blood cells in the circulatory system during winter dormancy. This is probably an energy saving exercise as a combination of relatively high oxygen levels in the cold water, combined with low oxygen requirement (43mg/kg/hr at 5°C compared with 243mg/kg/hr at 20°C) means a high red blood cell count would be superfluous and could constitute a serious energy drain or it may be a mechanism to stop sludging and clot formation at a time of poor circulation. It is unlikely to be merely due to impaired osmoregulation because the water content of muscle actually reduces with lowered temperature – 82% at 11°C to 80% at 2°C. A lowered ambient temperature also affects the immune response (see 5.1.1)

A complete adjustment to lowered temperatures may take up to twenty days whereas high temperature adaptation is quicker, often within one day.

1.1.4 Sudden thermal stress

Given the option, fish exposed to a sudden, marked temperature stress would move along a temperature gradient away from that stimulus, towards an area of more appropriate temperature. However in aquaria or ponds this is often not an option, so the fish must attempt to adapt. This process happens in three stages.

1. Shock. The metabolic rate over compensates, either by increasing or decreasing abnormally.
2. The metabolic rate stabilises to its new rate over a period of several hours.
3. The rest of the physiological functions accommodate. This may take days to weeks.

The ability of fish to withstand thermal shock depends upon a number of factors including previous temperature adaptation, age, sex, nutritional status, dissolved oxygen levels and salinity. In extreme cases, the fish may be unable to adapt and will die.

A sudden, large rise in temperature dramatically increases metabolic rate creating an increased oxygen demand, and because the water holds less oxygen there is a reflex increase in heart rate. Adrenaline is released. The situation is compounded by the relatively low oxygen affinity of fish haemoglobin. Lactic acid builds up as the fish switch to anaerobic metabolic pathways, causing a fall in pH of the body fluids – an acidosis. At excessively high temperatures there is denaturation of proteins including enzymes, and alteration in the state of cell membrane lipids, which in the gills will cause osmoregulatory dysfunction. The toxicity of certain water constituents, such as NH_3 and heavy metals, is also increased.

A quick, dramatic lowering of ambient temperature does not allow the adaptive changes. Hypoxia results, secondary to lowered heart and respiratory rates. Osmoregulation is affected, the gill Na^+ pump fails, causing increased gill permeability and eventual renal failure. In goldfish this causes a rapid dilution of the blood with subsequent rupture of the red blood cells due to osmotic imbalance, with a consequent loss of haemoglobin. There may be an insufficient release of energy to support life, leading to a loss of consciousness. If this is not reversed then death will ensue.

Rapid changes in temperature either way will induce stress in these naturally hardy fish, suppressing their immune responses and decreasing their disease resistance. Interestingly some fish with infections will seek out areas of higher temperatures, performing a behavioural "fever" response. If given anti-pyretics their recovery is compromised. This can be used clinically, in that keeping fish at a temperature a degree or two higher than their PBT will often help their recovery (see 5.1.1).

At very low temperatures the bacteria in the biological filtration beds stop functioning, causing a rise in potentially toxic NH_3 and NO_2 levels. Fortunately at lower temperatures most of the ammonia occurs as the less toxic NH^{4+}. Conversely higher temperatures promote the formation of the more toxic NH_3.

1.2.1 Water chemistry
In practice pure water is never encountered. In fact fish are swimming in a solution of a variety of substances including calcium (Ca^{2+}), magnesium (Mg^{2+}), and sodium (Na^+) salts, as well as copper, iron and other trace elements. The actual composition of any given water sample will reflect its source. The main sources are:

1.2.2 Ground water
The composition of this water will reflect the local soil constituents and the underlying rock strata e.g. chalk will raise the pH and hardness; excessive leaf litter will tend to reduce the pH because of organic acids. Pesticide runoff can be a problem.

1.2.3 Rain water
This should be soft (low mineral content) and of neutral pH. However industrial air pollution can release toxic gases eg. SO_2, which dissolve in rainwater producing strong acids such as H_2SO_4 (sulphuric acid) – acid rain!

1.2.4 Tap water
Looks good enough to drink, and indeed that's what it is designed for – *not* for fish. Water chemistry not only depends upon its source but also on any subsequent treatment. This can include:

i)   Coagulation – The binding together of suspended particles.
ii) Filtration. The physical removal of suspended particles.
iii) pH adjustment to around 7.0.
iv) Addition of chlorine or chloramine as a disinfectant.
v)   Water softening.
vi) Other chemicals, such as pesticides to control crustacea, or high NO_3 levels from agricultural runoff.

1.3.1 pH
In simple terms, this is a measure of the acidity of a given sample of water, given on a scale of 0-14. The acidity of water is proportional to the hydrogen ion (H^+) content. Points to note are:

i)   pH less than 7.0 = acid.
     pH 7.0 = neutral.
     pH greater than 7.0 = alkaline.

ii) The scale is logarithmic, therefore a pH change of 1 unit = a 10 fold change in (H^+), and a 2 unit change = 100 fold. Therefore water at a pH=7 is ten times more acidic than water at pH=8.
iii) Alkaline water, with a pH greater than 7.0, has a relative lack of H^+. However alkalinity is occasionally used to describe the amount of negatively charged ions

present. Principally this is the hydroxyl ion OH^-, but also includes the HCO_3^- and CO_3^{2-} and other ions. Used this way, alkalinity is an expression of water hardness (see 1.4.2).

1.3.2 Koi and goldfish are very adaptable accepting a broad pH range, although the region of 7.5-8.0 is preferred. The pH can have physiological effects on fish, primarily osmoregulation. Na^+ is exchanged at the gills for H^+, although it is not known whether this is an active or passive process. If the pH falls, then the H^+ ion concentration increases and Na^+ is not taken up across the gill membranes. This produces an osmoregulatory imbalance and an acidosis. High calcium (Ca^{2+}) levels reduce the permeability of the gill epithelium to both H^+ and Na^+ and so is protective. Gill tissue is at a pH 7.4. If the pH falls, then the Bohr effect will reduce the affinity of the red blood cell haemoglobin for oxygen. Also the Root effect gives a shift in the dissociation curve increasing the rate of deoxygenation.

Acidic water can cause paling of black areas in koi. If the water is very alkaline the black areas expand secondary to melanocyte expansion.

1.3.3 Environmental effects of pH
Dissolved ammonia is in equilibrium, and at pH greater than 8.5 most of it is as the toxic NH_3 (see 1.6.2). Acidic water increases the solubility, and hence the toxicity of the heavy metals zinc, copper and aluminium.

1.3.4 Causes of low pH
i)   Infrequent water changes. Primarily a problem in aquaria, over a period of time there is a build up of carbonic acid from respiration, and organic acids from metabolism. Biological filtration can also bring about a fall in pH because, as ammonia (NH_3) is converted to nitrite (NO_2), there is a fall in OH^- and a rise in H^+. There can also be a build up in debris with its resultant decomposition causing a fall in pH.
ii) Acid rainfall on to ponds.
iii) Acidic runoff from surrounding soil.

1.3.5 Causes of high pH
i)   Excessive algal and plant growth. During the day dissolved CO_2 is used up during photosynthesis. Once this has all gone, then HCO_3^- is utilised. HCO_3^- is a major buffer, so as levels fall there is a resultant pH increase. At night CO_2 released during respiration forms HCO_3^- ions and therefore the pH falls. This oscillation in pH gives characteristic pH pulses over a 24 hour period, typical of heavily planted ponds.
ii) Untreated/unsealed cement in ponds. This can produce a huge pH rise, up to 10 or 11, and can take many, many years to stabilise.

1.3.6 Fish can acclimate to a pH outside the normal range if adjusted slowly. This can happen in aquaria over a period of time if no water changes are performed – if one adds new fish in this situation they immediately show signs of distress and may die. One should avoid making sudden changes in pH. Unfortunately the Water Supply Companies may cause problems if they are able to draw water from different areas, as you may be supplied with water of different pH from one day to the next.

1.3.7 Acidosis
If the pH is less than 5.5, especially if the change is rapid, then fish will show increased excitability, occasionally even jumping from the water as a result of irritation to the gills and skin. There is an increase in mucus production often accompanied by erythema especially at the ventral area. A falling pH reduces the bioavailability of oxygen (see 1.3.2.), causing the fish to gasp at the surface. Mucus clogs the gills, reducing gaseous exchange. At pH less than 5.0 colloids are deposited on the gills.

1.3.8 Alkalosis
This occurs at pH greater than 8.0 to 9.0. Again there is excitability and mucus production. Fins become frayed. Gill epithelium hypertrophy may be seen. Remember that at pH greater than 8.5 NH_3 becomes more toxic.

1.3.9 Management of pH
pH test kits are readily available, as are electronic pH meters. One should remember to record the time of day of sampling.

If the pH is too low (acidic) :

i)   Regular water changes. Try not to alter the pH by more than 0.3 units per day.
ii) Buffering salts are available.
iii) Increase aeration. This allows CO_2 levels to fall as it comes out of solution at the surface.
iv) Denitrification. This reverses the acidification by biological filtration.

If the pH is too high (alkaline):

i)   Regular water changes.
ii) Buffering salts or other buffers eg. aquarium peat (not garden peat!).
iii) Avoid excessive plant or algal growths.

1.4.1 Hardness
The hardness of water is a measure of its mineral content.

1.4.2 Definitions
These are a potential source of confusion.
Carbonate hardness – ^oKH – associated with the concentrations of CO_3^{2-}, HCO_3^- and OH- salts.

Non-carbonate hardness – ^oNKH – associated with SO_4^{2-}, Cl^- and NO_3^{2-}.

Total carbonate – ^oGH – This is carbonate + non-carbonate.
In some German texts however, one may see ^oGH as the total degrees German hardness. More usually this is represented as ^odH and refers to calcium oxide concentration! In this text, ^oGH is used to represent total hardness and not German hardness.

Alkalinity. Another measure of carbonate hardness; measures CO_3^{2-}, HCO_3^- and OH^-, therefore it is also a measure of the waters ability to neutralise acid (see 1.3.1)
Temporary hardness. Usually refers to HCO_3^- levels. On boiling, HCO_3^- comes out of solution as an insoluble CO_3 precipitate, usually as $CaCO_3$ or $MgCO_3$.
N.B. HCO_3 is a buffer: e.g.

$$OH^- + HCO_3^- \rightarrow H_2O + CO_3^{2-} \text{ or } H^+ + HCO_3^- \rightarrow H_2O + CO_2$$

Permanent hardness. The mineral content not removed by boiling.

$CaCO_3$ is the most abundant mineral found in water, therefore hardness is usually expressed as mg $CaCO_3$/l. Although several different scales of measurement have been established, they are readily convertible.

1° Hardness (USA) = 1.0mg/l $CaCO_3$
1° Clark (UK) = 143mg/l $CaCO_3$
1^odH (German and = CaO) = 17.9mg/l $CaCO_3$
1 milliequivalent (meq) = 50.0mg/l $CaCO_3$

Water Hardness Values

Very soft	0-50 mg/l CaCO3
Moderately soft	50-100 mg/l CaCO3
Slightly hard	100-150mg/l CaCO3
Moderately hard	150-200mg/l CaCO3
Hard	200-300mg/l CaCO3
Very hard	300+mg/l CaCO3

Test kits for water hardness are readily available.

1.4.3 Conductivity
Electrical conductivity gives an idea of dissolved mineral levels. Unit = microsiemens ($\mu S/cm$), and a normal range would be around $180 – 480$ μS. This is usually used with marine aquaria where small changes in dissolved mineral content can be significant, but it can be relevant to koi at importation (see 1.4.6) or monitoring dissolved salt levels during treatment.

1.4.4 Physiological importance of hardness
i) Ca reduces the permeability of the gill epithelial cell membranes to Na^+ and H^+, and importantly, to NH_3.
ii) Increasing KH = increased alkalinity and therefore potentiates NH_3 toxicity.
iii) Increasing hardness reduces osmoregulatory stress by lessening the osmotic gradient.
iv) High levels of hardness reduce the toxicity of dissolved Cu and Zn due to competition by Ca and Mg at gill absorption sites.
v) In very soft water, low Ca concentrations can result in poor bone formation and increased disease susceptibility. Minimum levels should be 12.5mg/l $CaCO_3$.
vi) Very hard water can reduce egg viability. Since egg hardening is secondary to the intake of ions down an osmotic gradient, increasing hardness will reduce the osmotic gradient.
vii) The presence of high levels of incorrect ions can cause problems. Certain water softening compounds are ion-exchangers, swapping Ca ions for Na ions. If this water is used then the high Na concentration will induce a net loss of $H+$ from the gills, possibly leading to an alkalosis

1.4.5 Correcting water hardness
In practice this is not usually necessary because koi are tolerant of a range of hardness values. In addition the vast majority of waters in the UK are moderately hard because they are taken from calciferous aquifers i.e. from chalk or limestone rock formations. To increase water hardness, use Ca based salts. Also calciferous substrates such as dolomite will maintain water hardness. To reduce water hardness, top up with rainwater, or use ion-exchange resins (see proviso at 1.4.4) or reverse osmosis. These measures are rarely necessary with koi.

1.4.6 Salinity
Certain "physiological" salts are marketed which contain salts normally found in the body tissues. They can be used to reduce osmotic stress by reducing the osmotic gradient between the fish and its surroundings. $MgSO_4$ is ideal for reducing this osmotic stress because the Mg will not upset the acid-base balance of the fish whilst the SO_4 will not contribute to the KH and so will not potentiate the effects of NH_3. In my experience it works extremely well, especially with ascitic fish. Salts can also help by reducing NH_3 and NO_2 toxicity. Ca^{2+} reduces the permeability of the gill membranes to NH_3, whilst CL- competes with NO_2 at absorption sites on the gill epithelial membranes.

Both salinity and water hardness have an effect on osmoregulation. However common salt which contains only sodium chloride, has no effect on water hardness. Sea salt and other physiological salts contain other elements and so contribute to both the total hardness (°GH) and conductivity.

1g of sea salt per 1.0 litre of water raises the total hardness by 9-10 °dH, or 161 – 179 mg/l $CaCO_3$, and in general 1.0 mg/l $CaCO_3$ increases conductivity by 1.84 µS/cm. 1g of common or sea salt increases conductivity by 1 800 to 2 000 µS/cm.

In some cases fish are imported in water with added salt. To reduce the osmotic stress on these fish when transferred out of their transport bags it may be necessary to back calculate the dose rate of salt being used so that this can be mimicked in their new water. If we know the conductivity (µS/cm) and, from the above, we assume that:-

a) The average equivalent for conductivity of 1g of salt per 1.0l of water = 1 900
b) The conductivity equivalent for 1.0 mg $CaCO_3$ = 1.84

Then:-

$$\text{Salt concentration in use (g/l)} = \frac{\text{Conductivity} - (\text{Total Hardness mg/l CaCO3} \times 1.84)}{1\ 900}$$

1.5.1 The Nitrogen Cycle

The waste products of nitrogen metabolism are the commonest causes of poor water quality and toxicities encountered. The concept of the nitrogen cycle as relevant to fishkeeping, is given in Fig 1 below.

Problems arise in aquaria and ponds because:

i) High levels of nitrogen are put into the system via fish food and, in certain areas, high ambient levels of NO_3 in the tapwater.
ii) There is relatively little denitrification, therefore toxic levels of NO_3 can build up.
iii) High stocking levels results in high NH_3 production.
iv) Water quality changes. Over a period of time pH will often fall, reducing the efficacy of bacterial action. This stops at pH of less than 5.5 (ideal = pH 9.0) Temperature is also important because the bacteria work best at tropical temperatures and not at pond or "coldwater" temperatures.

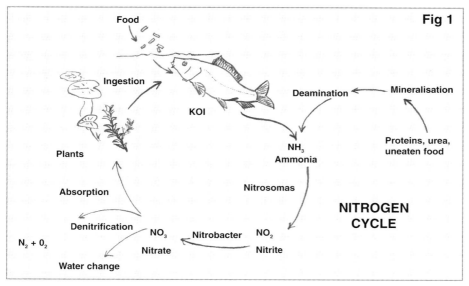

Fig 1

NITROGEN CYCLE

vi) Channelling of water through restricted areas of undergravel filters. Goldfish and koi will naturally grub around through the substrate, redistributing it at will. This behaviour can short circuit undergravel filters.

1.6.1 Ammonia
Sources of ammonia are :
i) The end product of nitrogen metabolism of fish and many other aquatic animals. Excreted both across the gill membranes and via the kidneys.
ii) Bacterial action. Several genera of bacteria e.g. *Achromobacter, Micrococcus* and *Flavobacterium* use complex proteins and protein breakdown products, for instance from uneaten food, as substrates, converting them to NH_3 in a two stage process.
Stage I = mineralisation where proteins, urea, uric acid are broken down into amino acids.
Stage II = deamination, where the amino acids are converted to NH_3.

1.6.2 Dissolved ammonia exists in a state of equilibrium, between the ionised NH^{4+} ion and the non-ionised NH_3. The balance of the equilibrium is affected by temperature, pH and, to a lesser extent, salinity.

$$NH^{4+} + OH \rightleftharpoons NH_3 + H_2O$$

This shift has clinical significance because the ionised NH^{4+} cannot readily cross cell membranes and is therefore relatively less toxic whereas NH_3 can easily cross these barriers causing serious problems.

1.6.3 Chemical and electronic test kits are readily available. However these usually measure TOTAL ammonium and not NH_3 or NH^{4+}. Some measure ammonium-nitrogen, with conversion methods to total ammonium provided with the kits. It is the level of unionised NH_3 that concerns us most. It is considered that levels less than 0.02mg/l (ppm) are optimum. Table 1.1 shows the levels of total ammonia (mg/l) at a range of pH and temperature (deg.C) values that maintain unionised ammonia at 0.02mg/l or less.

1.6.4 As mentioned in 1.6.2, ionised NH^{4+} cannot cross cell membranes and so is believed to be of limited toxicity. NH_3, however, is readily diffusible and is associated with specific pathologies. NH_3 is irritant, inducing a reactive hyperplasia of the secondary gill lamellae. This thickening affects the water flow between the lamellae causing channelling to occur. The irritation induces excessive mucus production, further reducing the water flow and increasing the sites for bacterial and parasitic attachment. NH_3 is diffusible, so as the levels in the environment increase the diffusion gradient is reduced and endogenous levels build up to dangerous levels.

TABLE 1

pH Temp °C	6.0	6.5	7.0	7.5	8.0	8.5	9.0
0	250	77	24	7.7	2.4	0.78	0.1
5	154	50	16	5.0	1.6	0.52	0.07
10	105	34	11	3.4	1.1	0.36	0.05
15	74	23	7.5	2.3	0.75	0.25	0.04
20	50	16	5.0	1.6	0.52	0.18	0.04
25	35	11	7.5	1.1	0.37	0.13	0.03
30	25	8.0	2.5	0.8	0.27	0.10	0.03

The central nervous system (CNS) is at special risk. Goldfish are able to compensate by immediately switching over to urea excretion and possibly by increasing CNS glycolysis to provide more substrates for transammination reactions and the formation of amino acids to reduce the levels of free NH_3. These mechanisms may give rise to some of the signs seen in NH_3 toxicity, but it is a trade-off to deal with the more harmful NH_3. Kidney pathology can occur if exposure is prolonged, with ceroid deposits in the excretory part of the kidney and hyaline deposits in the proximal tubules. Liver pathology may be seen. Goldfish seem unaffected by total ammonia levels of 0.025mg/l, but 10% die at 0.04mg/l within 24 hours. Affected fish stop swimming, settle on the bottom and eventually turn on to their sides, forming a "U" shape. Opercular movements slow progressively until death occurs. Even at this late stage some goldfish are able to recover if placed into NH_3 free water.

1.6.5 Specific instances of ammonia toxicity

i) Following importation. After several hours in transit, the water in the containers will have changed because of a fall in temperature, a fall in pH due to expired CO_2, and a rise in excreted NH_3 – however the low temperatures and low pH will ensure that most of the ammonia is present as NH^{4+}. Caring importers will gradually raise the temperature and even add buffers to the water to increase the pH to mimic ambient tapwater conditions but both these actions will cause a shift towards NH_3 and an acute ammonia toxicity. This situation can be avoided by transferring fish to similar but ammonia free water BEFORE correcting the water quality.

ii) New tank/pond syndrome – see 1.7.4.

iii) Sudden, marked overstocking. This produces an ammonia surge because the bacterial filtration needs time to adjust to the increased ammonia load.

1.6.6 Correction of high ammonia levels
i)   Dilution by partial water changes.
ii) Improvement/addition of biological filtration such as addition of commercial bacterial preparations.
iii) Ion-exchange materials such as the natural compound zeolite.
iv) Improvement of stocking levels, feeding regimes and general husbandry to remove debris and uneaten food.

1.7.1 Nitrite
The main source is as a bi-product of metabolism from *Nitrosomas* bacteria. These aerobic bacteria oxidise dissolved NH_3 to NO_2.

$$2NH^{4+} + 2OH^- + 3O_2 \rightarrow 2H^+ + 2NO_2^- + 4H_2O$$

This reaction is not pH dependent. Any effect of temperature is only secondary to its effects on bacterial metabolism.

1.7.2 Test kits and probes are readily available. Some measure nitrite-nitrogen. A conversion factor for a true NO_2 reading will be included in such kits.

1.7.3 Nitrite levels greater than 0.2mg/l are toxic to fish. Levels over 0.5mg/l are fatal. NO_2 ions bind irreversibly to haemoglobin, forming the stable compound methaemoglobin. Affected fish gasp at the surface and the gills are a characteristic brown colour. With long term exposure to sublethal levels of NO_2, fish become anaemic with a predisposition to bacterial infections.

1.7.4 Specific instances of NO₂ toxicity

i)   Breakdown of biological filtration. This may occur following antibiotic treatment (lowered bacterial numbers), exposure to low temperatures (reduced bacterial action) or incorrect cleaning of filter media. This latter problem can arise either from excessive cleaning of the filter media causing a physical removal of the nitrosomas bacteria, or rinsing under tap water. Remember chlorine is specifically added to tap water to kill bacteria therefore it is best to rinse the media in old pond or aquarium water.
ii) New Tank/Pond Syndrome. Classically this is the excessive overstocking of a new aquarium or pond, although a sudden or marked overstocking of an established set up can cause similar problems. Biological filters need at least 14 days at ideal conditions (pH 7.5+ and 30°C) to respond to increased NH_3 levels. At 10°C this can take 4 - 8 weeks. With too many fish, ammonia levels build up to toxic levels; then, after a time lag during which the *Nitrosomas* multiply up, NO_2 rises, again often to dangerous levels because there is an insufficient *Nitrobacter* population to further convert this to NO_3. This is a common beginners mistake. Unscrupulous dealers selling "just add water" packages consisting of tank, lights, filter and fish ,can lead beginners into this problem. Establishment of the correct filter flora can

be achieved by the addition of commercial freeze-dried or aqueous suspension of filter bacteria, or use some gravel/filter media from established filter beds to seed new filters. Alternatively goldfish are relatively NH_3/NO_2 tolerant and so one can gradually mature a filter by SLOWLY building up the numbers of fish, monitoring NH_3 and NO_2 levels daily to make sure they stay within an acceptable range.

1.7.5 Correction of high NO_2 levels

i) Partial water changes.
ii) Improve or install biological filtration.
iii) Improve feeding regime, stocking and husbandry.
iv) Toxicity of NO_2 can be reduced by increasing the chloride (Cl^-) ions in solution, usually by addition of NaCl. Cl^- ions compete with NO_2 ion binding sites at the gills. Also salt affects the ionocytes of the gill tissue such that it can improve their capacity to eliminate NH_3 and NO_2. The best ratio seems to be 5:1 $Cl:NO_2$.

To calculate required amount:-
Cl (mg/l) needed = $(5x[NO_2]) - [Cl_a])$
where $[NO_2]$ = concentration of NO_2 in mg/l and $[Cl_a]$ = concentration of Cl^- already present in mg/l

Both $[NO_2]$ and $[Cl_a]$ can be measured with commercial test kits, although in practice unless salt has already been used, $[Cl_a]$ is likely to be negligible (see 1.4.6).

Once the [Cl] needed has been calculated, then:

Salt (NaCl) needed/kg = V x [Cl] where V = volume of pond/aquarium in l and [Cl] is the amount of Cl needed.
Alternatively aim for a 0.3% NaCl solution = 3kg/1 000litres of pond water. High levels of dietary vitamin C offer some protection.

1.8.1 Nitrate Sources:

i) End product of nitrification, completed by aerobic *Nitrobacter* bacteria.
NO_3 is produced as a further oxidation of NO_2
$2NO_2^- + O_2^- \rightarrow 2NO_3$. Any temperature effects are secondary to its effects on *Nitrobacter* metabolism.
ii) Natural water sources and even tap water can have high levels of NO_3, possibly arising from contamination of water sources with agricultural fertilisers, up to concentrations as high as 130mg/l.

1.8.2 Test kits and probes are readily available. Those kits which measure nitrate-nitrogen will have a conversion factor supplied.

1.8.3 Considered less toxic than NH_3 or NO_2, nevertheless it can still cause problems at high concentrations. OATA (Ornamental Aquatic Trade Association) recommend that NO_3 levels should not exceed 50mg/l above the ambient tap water levels. 1600 mg/l NO_3 is toxic to goldfish. Knowledge of its toxicity is limited, although at high concentrations the effects may be osmotic. It is known to be a stressor and so can lead to secondary complications.

1.8.4 Specific instances of high NO_3

i)   High ambient tap water levels – always check NO_3 levels in supply tap water.
ii) Insufficient water changes, therefore NO_3 levels can be a good indicator of husbandry standards.
iii) Inadvertent feeding of fish with plant fertiliser by neighbours/relatives. Pelleted fertilisers can look a lot like fish food!

1.8.5 Correction of high NO_3 levels

i)   Regular water changes, replacing with water of a lower NO_3 content.
ii) Ion exchange resins or reverse osmosis. Reverse osmosis involves the forcing of tap water across a semi-permeable membrane such that only pure water is extruded on the other side.
iii) Increase the plant density. NO_3 is an important plant food. Many koi keepers utilise vegetable filters in the form of water cress, an avid NO_3 feeder, grown at the filter outlet.
iv) Denitrification. Certain anaerobic bacteria reduce NO_3 to free nitrogen and free oxygen. This will happen to a greater or lesser extent in any established pond or aquarium; some filter media are designed to provide surfaces allowing colonisation of both aerobic nitrifying and anaerobic denitrifying bacteria. Denitrification is used extensively in marine aquaria where NO_3 is more toxic due to the increased salinity, but it is rarely used with koi and goldfish, which are naturally more resistant.

1.9.1 Oxygen

Levels of dissolved oxygen are an often-neglected aspect of water quality. Goldfish and koi are well adapted to low oxygen concentrations by a variety of metabolic and behavioural adaptations – indeed this is probably their main key to survival in garden ponds and household aquaria. Remember that although oxygen constitutes 20% of atmospheric air, it is relatively insoluble in water such that there is 20 to 30 times less oxygen in a given volume of water than in the equivalent volume of air.

1.9.2 Sources

i) Diffusion from atmospheric air at the air/water interface. This is usually at the surface of the body of water.
ii) As a biproduct of photosynthesis from submerged aquatic plants.

iii) Some commercial trout and salmon farms pump liquid oxygen into the water, timed to coincide with episodes of low dissolved oxygen. This is economically non-viable for goldfish and koi except for large commercial concerns, nor is it likely to be absolutely necessary.

1.9.3 Many factors affect the final levels of dissolved oxygen. These include :

i)   Temperature. Oxygen solubility decreases as temperature increases. At 10°C oxygen levels are 11.28mg/l, whereas at 20°C it will be reduced to 9.08mg/l.

ii) Salinity. In water at 10°C with no dissolved salt, oxygen levels are 11.28mg/l whereas in a 2% NaCl solution (a salinity of 20ppt or 20g/l) oxygen levels fall to 9.93mg/l.

iii) Altitude. With increasing altitude there is less atmospheric oxygen, therefore its partial pressure will be reduced and so less oxygen will dissolve into the water.

iv) Surface area. This breaks down into a number of factors. Actual surface area is important as this is the main site of gaseous exchange – it is surface area rather than water volume which will govern stocking densities. Turbulence in the form of waves, wind action, air bubbles and water currents increase oxygen uptake by increasing the surface area available and by thinning the water surface layer – the laminar layer, allowing easier gaseous exchange. Water currents also bring more of the water volume into contact with the air/water interface. This is primarily how air stones help to improve oxygen levels – the amount of oxygen absorbed from the bubbles is negligible. Only 1% of oxygen is absorbed from these bubbles per metre rise in the water column so this effect will only be significant in deep waters.

v)   Numbers of plants. During daylight all plants, including algae, photosynthesise releasing oxygen as a biproduct. They, like the fish, are also respiring and using up oxygen but so much more is released that waters can become supersaturated with oxygen. During the night however, plants are no longer photosynthesising but respiration continues and can cause significant falls in oxygen levels, which reach their lowest levels just before dawn.

vi) Further to (v), other organisms including the fish are continually utilising oxygen. An often-neglected group is the aerobic bacteria cultivated in biological filters, which in total require vast amounts of oxygen.

1.9.4 Redox potential

Large amounts of decaying material can reduce the available dissolved oxygen content. This gives rise to the concept of Redox Potential. This is a measure of a sample of water's ability (or potential) for reduction or oxidation. It is a measure of the electrons in that sample. Its relevance to koi keeping is that a body of water with a high redox potential is of high quality, with plenty of surplus oxygen. Low redox potential waters would have low oxygen levels, with excessive waste materials incompletely oxidised or broken down. Poorly maintained ponds with large amounts of organic waste from overstocking or leaf litter will have a low redox potential.

Redox is measured on the p∈ scale of 0 to 42, with 0 as the lowest oxidising (highest reducing) ability and 42 the most powerful oxidising potential. Normal values range from around 27 to 32.

1.9.5 Test kits and probes are available.

1.9.6 Koi and goldfish are able to cope with oxygen levels over a wide range. In the wild, fish are able to swim from areas with incorrect oxygen levels but ponds and aquaria are rarely large enough to allow this behaviour. OATA recommend 8.0mg/l with a minimum of 5.0mg/l although this latter value should be higher for eggs and fry. Problems can occur with oxygen values outside this range, and even towards the lower end of this range although one may not see signs of hypoxia, various metabolic functions such as growth and reproduction may be severely affected.

i) Insufficient oxygen. If dissolved oxygen concentrations are marginal the situation can be worsened in warmer water not only because the water holds less oxygen but also there is an increased utilisation by the fish – carp kept at 2°C utilise 7.2mg O_2 per kg bodyweight with this rocketing to 300mg O_2 per kg at 30°C. Larger fish with greater bodyweight have disproportionately higher oxygen demands and it is these that show signs, and in the worst cases die, first. If oxygen levels fall too low the fish become hypoxic and will start to gasp at the surface. They may well congregate around filter outlets and other areas where the increased water turbulence will create a localised area of oxygenation. Koi are able to switch to alternative anaerobic pathways although prolonged exposure to these conditions risks an acidosis secondary to lactic acid build up. Heart rate slows but the stroke volume increases. The ventilation volume also increases. Should the fish become progressively more hypoxic it may show a frantic escape response. Once oxygen levels reach critically low levels the fish will respond by increasing the opercular ventilation rate, which in itself incurs an oxygen debt. If all these are unsuccessful the fish will become comatose and die. Classically, fish that have died in this way, have flared operculae, wide open mouths and pale gills.

ii) Supersaturation with oxygen results in Gas Bubble Disease. Because oxygen is so insoluble in water any event which causes a decrease in the partial pressure of the dissolved oxygen in waters which are supersaturated will cause an immediate dissolution of oxygen. This manifests itself as obvious bubbles forming in the blood vessels, especially of the fins with a resultant fraying and haemorrhage, and occasionally behind the eye, although they may occur on all body surfaces. If the swimbladder is involved the fish may loose its balance. Usually the fish come to no harm.

1.9.7 Specific causes of low oxygen levels
i) Overstocking.
ii) Poor husbandry. Excessive debris produces a low redox potential (see 2.9.4). Rotting leaves of deciduous trees in the autumn can be a particular problem.

iii) Warm thundery weather can be a problem because of the combination of low air pressures and higher water temperatures.

iv) Inadequate water circulation or "aeration".

v) Heavy plant growths and algal blooms can utilise the majority of oxygen during the hours of darkness.

vi) Treatments with certain chemicals. Formalin removes oxygen from the water. Malachite green can produce the signs of hypoxia but it is actually working at a cellular level on the respiratory enzymes, so increasing dissolved oxygen concentrations has no effect.

1.9.8 Management of low oxygen levels

i) Correct stocking densities.

ii) Improve water circulation and increase water turbulence with e.g. air stones, venturis, fountains. Do not turn these off at night.

iii) Reduce plant growth and treat algal blooms as necessary.

iv) In aquaria consider the feasibility of reducing high water temperatures by floating plastic bags containing ice in the tanks.

v) Install trickle filters if possible, thereby allowing the filter bacteria to use atmospheric oxygen rather than dissolved oxygen.

1.9.9 Causes of oxygen supersaturation

i) Exuberant photosynthesis during daylight hours.

ii) Mixing of air and water under pressure. In nature this would occur at the bottom of waterfalls but is unlikely to be a problem with ornamental carp.

1.9.10 Management of oxygen supersaturation

i) Improve circulation allowing the excess dissolved oxygen to dissipate into the atmosphere.

ii) Control of plant and algal growths.

iii) Symptomatic treatment of damaged fins and skin.

1.10.1 Carbon dioxide

This is a bi-product of aerobic respiration and is released by fish, plants and bacteria. It is also utilised by plants for photosynthesis during daylight hours.

1.10.2 Unlike oxygen it is highly soluble in water. Dissolved CO_2 is in equilibrium with carbonic acid H_2CO_3 and the bicarbonate ion HCO_3^-.

$$CO_2 + H_2O \rightleftharpoons H_2CO_3 \rightleftharpoons HCO_3^- + H^+$$

23

1.10.3 CO_2 is freely diffusible across the gill membranes, with CO_2 produced from respiration maintaining the diffusion gradient necessary for its loss from the fish. In cases of high ambient CO_2 levels this diffusion gradient is reduced, causing an increase in blood CO_2 levels and a fall in blood pH. This fall in pH reduces the affinity of haemoglobin for oxygen, increases the rate of deoxygenation and reduces the rate of oxygen uptake even in the presence of adequate oxygen levels. Prolonged exposure to free CO_2 levels greater than 10-20mg/l has been associated with nephrocalcinosis, mineral deposits forming in the renal tubules, collecting ducts and ureters.

1.10.4 Specific cases of high environmental CO_2

i)   High stocking densities where there are high rates of respiration. High CO_2 concentrations are especially found at the surface layers.
ii) Heavily planted ponds. During the night photosynthesis stops, but the plants continue to respire. CO_2 levels reach a maximum prior to dawn.
iii) Decomposition of high levels of organic matter.
iv) Ice forming over of the water surface reduces gaseous exchange.

1.10.5 Management of CO_2 levels

i)   Reduce stocking densities.
ii) Control plant or algal growth.
iii) Improve circulation or aeration. This allows an increased dispersal of free CO_2 from solution.
iv) Maintenance of an ice free area of pond surface during winter.

1.11.1 Chlorine
Added by Water Companies as an oxidising agent and antibacterial. In solution it forms hypochlorous acid and hypochlorite, the relative concentrations of which are pH, and temperature, dependant. At 25°C, and a pH less than 7.5 the more toxic hypochlorous acid predominates whilst above pH 7.5 it is hypochlorite. Decreasing temperatures favour hypochlorous acid formation. Chlorine is not stable in solution, and so water companies calculate the dosage such that there is still an active concentration at the furthest point down the line. To improve stability chlorine can be combined with NH_3 to produce chloramine which is more stable in solution, and has the toxicity problems associated with NH_3 as well as chlorine. Chlorine seems to work at a cellular level, chlorinating cell membranes and enzymes. Goldfish and koi are particularly sensitive to chlorine with levels of 4.0ppm causing mortalities within eight hours of exposure. Constant exposure to even lower levels of 0.2 to 0.3ppm, which are often found in tap water, will kill these fish after around three weeks.

Affected fish show an escape reaction, become discoloured and there may be epithelial burns of the fins, gills and skin; the fish eventually becoming weakened and dying of respiratory failure. High levels can cause peracute deaths with no obvious clinical signs. Levels as low as 0.002ppm will induce gill hyperplasia on chronic exposure. Aerating water well before using in water changes, or leaving it to stand for 24 hours should dissipate most of the chlorine. Commercial tap water conditioners are available which contain sodium thiosulphate which will actively bind any chlorine present. Zeolite can be used to absorb any NH_3 if chloramine is used.

1.12.1 Heavy metals

This list includes lead, copper, iron, zinc cadmium and aluminium. A certain level of dissolved heavy metals is normal as these can leach into the water not only from the rock formations at source but from a variety of other sources such as lead or copper domestic water piping. Certain proprietary fish medications contain copper. Toxicity depends upon the water pH and the temperature, as the lower the pH and the higher the temperature the more soluble these metals become. At high pH values (greater than 7.0) iron precipitates out as iron hydroxide, coating the gills causing acute respiratory distress and even death. Aluminium, too, is toxic at a pH over 8.

Water hardness and synergisms or antagonisms with other dissolved substances can also be important and so it is very difficult to give accurate ideas of toxicity levels. Again, because many of these toxicites are chronic, and can result from cumulative exposure, testing of water levels and parameters may be of limited value. Post-mortem sampling will be the best way to gain a definitive diagnosis.

Fortunately the majority of tap water in the UK is stabilised at a pH of around 7.0 and is so hard that the piping gains a coating of $CaCO_3$ reducing the absorption of metals from the pipe walls. Chronic exposure to damaging levels can lead to pathology in the gills, kidneys and liver. In turn this can lead to osmotic imbalance, respiratory distress, poor growth rates, deformities and a fall in reproductive performance. Hatchling fry may have deformities. Normal immunity is suppressed increasing susceptibility to secondary infections. Chronic exposure to toxic levels of cadmium, mercury, lead and zinc have been associated with anaemias. Copper, and to a lesser extent aluminium, depresses phagocytic activity. Acute episodes can cause an entire wipe-out especially of younger fish. Acute zinc toxicity of fish transferred to galvanised containers is occasionally seen. If one suspects heavy metal toxicity then analysis of post mortem material should be undertaken. Suggested tissue samples are:

Lead :	Kidney, gills, liver and muscle.
Mercury :	Liver, gills, kidney and muscle.
Cadmium:	Liver, kidney and gills.
Nickel :	Liver, gills, kidney and muscle.
Chromium:	Liver, kidney, gills and muscle.
Tin:	Liver, brain and muscle.
Copper:	Gills and liver.
Zinc:	Liver, gills and kidneys.
Aluminium:	Gills and liver.

Using a proprietary water conditioner with each water change can reduce the risks of heavy metal toxicities, as many of these contain chelating agents which will bind up any metals ions into complexes harmless to the fish. Commercially available water purifiers can be used for pre-treatment of water changes. These employ a variety of resins and carbon based filters to remove deleterious substances including heavy metals. Do not use water from the hot tap as the higher temperatures mean it will contain increased levels of dissolved heavy metals from the storage tank or pipework.

Chapter Two
Examination

A good clinical examination is an important cornerstone of making a diagnosis. Equally important is the history of the problem, plus water quality information. If a group of fish is affected it is often best to sacrifice one or two of the worst affected ones and perform a post-mortem. However it is best to do this immediately after euthanasia (see 3.4.1). Fish start to autolyse (decompose) very quickly after death, especially if the water is warm, and bacterial invasion of the carcass is very quick making bacteriological studies of limited use by the time a couple of hours has elapsed. The gills deteriorate very rapidly and the outer layers of skin including the mucus layer come away so much information is rapidly lost. Freezing destroys most useful information and thawing renders the fish unsuitable for histopathological examination. At best, placing the fish in a cool place such as a refrigerator will buy some time, but not much.

2.1.1 Examination procedures in the live fish

2.1.2 External examination
If possible observe the fish in its home pond or environment. If several fish are affected consider a water quality problem as well as a possibility of an infectious disease. It may be that only fish of certain species (in mixed displays) or certain sizes/ages are affected.

A koi should swim strongly and determinedly, and if others are present it should shoal with them. If the water is warm enough then most healthy koi are willing to feed. Fish separating themselves off from the rest of the shoal, or hanging around filtration outlets where the oxygen levels are highest must be suspect. Loss of appetite may be the first sign of impending problems and such koi should be examined closely. Koi struggling to swim or to maintain an even keel in the water may be weak or anaemic, or may have swimbladder disorders. Other disorders such as convulsions, abnormal swimming patterns and paralysis should be noted.

Healthy koi are usually well muscled with a smooth, symmetrical body outline and clean looking colours. Fish that have lost much muscle mass appear to be "big-headed" because of their relatively thin bodies. Some koi have naturally deep bodies and appear fat; other causes of swelling of the body cavity include ascites (dropsy – see later this section), ovarian enlargement in females ready to spawn and internal neoplasia (tumours). Loss of symmetry may be due to spinal deformities or tumours. Loss of the smooth clear outline and a dulling of colours is often due to increased mucus production and one should consider ectoparasites or water quality problems, especially if accompanied by signs of pruritis (itchiness) where the fish will scratch or flick against objects and surfaces. Occasionally koi may leap clear of the water – some koi appear to enjoy this, whilst in others it can be a sign of an irritant problem. Obvious skin lesions such as ulcers or areas of raised scales should be noted. The main fins should largely be upright, especially the pectoral and dorsal fins. The occasional flick of the fins is nothing to worry about, but if they are permanently clamped close to the body, or there is much blood streaking, obvious damage or erosion then this should be noted.

Respiratory rate and quality should be assessed. Depending upon the level of activity of the fish it can vary, but obvious disease signs include excessively high ventilation rates, mucus strands trailing from beneath the operculae and such wide extension of the operculae that the underlying gill tissue may be seen. Be aware that in some individuals the operculae may not develop. This can be unilateral or bilateral. This is a congenital abnormality.

Next one needs to examine the koi close up. Catching koi can be stressful for the fish – see 5.2.1. Once caught, transfer the fish from net to wet towel on the floor (not a table as koi are strong and very slippery and can easily slip off a high table) and immediately cover the its head with the wet towel. Large fish may need to be sedated first – see Chapter 3. Once secured, examine surfaces of fish for obvious lesions – especially ventrally as this is often overlooked and is not visible from the poolside.

Skin scrapes can be taken at this time (Figs 2.2 and 2.3). Pay particular attention to those areas where water turbulence causes eddy currents as these are sites favoured by parasites. Such sites are the bases of the fins, or around the eyes.

Take any swabs for bacteriology from any suspect lesions. Loss of scales is a serious problem as it will be a breach in the fish's osmotic barrier.

Lift both operculae to examine the gills (Fig 2.4). Their colour should be a nice salmon pink to red, with no patches of discolouration or greying (due to mucus production) and there should be a smooth outline to the branchial arches and the comb-like rows of gill filaments. If possible examine the oral cavity (Fig 2.5).

Many clues as to the state of certain internal structures can be ascertained by a critical external examination. Koi are symmetrical about the midline so internal tumours may give rise to asymmetric swellings of the body cavity, or Mycobacterial infections can result in collapse of vertebrae giving rise to fish with deformities of the spinal column. A pinecone appearance is due to ascites, a build up of fluid in the coelomic cavity as a result of osmoregulation imbalance from severe renal, gill or multi-organ disease.

2.1.3 Faecal examination
Colour and consistency may vary with disease. Examine faeces microscopically with a light microscope for worm eggs, or Protozoa eg. *Eimeria*. Bacterial swabs are probably best taken from within the rectum to reduce the risk of contamination.

2.1.4 Catheterisation of the urogenital orifice can be useful to assess sperm or ovum quality in large koi.

2.2.1 Post-mortem examination

Before embarking on a post-mortem examination, one should take a couple of standard measurements. These are :-

Standard Length (SL). This is a linear measurement from the most rostral tip of the snout to the base of the caudal fin. Do not include the caudal fin or any projection of the lower jaw.

Fig 2.2 Take skin scrapes and swabs if appropriate.

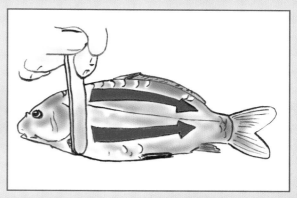

Fig 2.3 Arrows showing direction of skin scrape. Also scrape over operculum.

Fig 2.4 Lift both operculae to check gills.

Fig 2.5 Open the mouth and examine the oral cavity.

◄ Fig 2.1 Measure and weigh the koi and examine for obvious external lesions.
This doitsu ghost koi had a SL = 135mm and a weight of 85g.

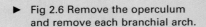
► Fig 2.6 Remove the operculum and remove each branchial arch.

Weight. By recording these measurements one not only begins to build up a picture of what constitutes normality for koi over a variety of size ranges, but it also helps one to estimate the weights of live fish, essential for appropriate drug dosage.

As a preliminary to a post-mortem examination, external structures should be examined as described for the live fish (see 2.1.2 above and Fig 2.1). However one now has the opportunity to take more invasive samples and biopsies of any obvious lesions (see 2.3.1).

Examine the oral cavity. Koi do not have teeth on the premaxilla and dentary bones – instead they have paired pharyngeal teeth ventrally, which grind against a thick, cornified pad (the carp stone) dorsally.

The gills in particular can now be examined closely. Start by removing the gill covers (operculae), and with a fine set of scissors snip each branchial arch at the top

► Fig 2.7 Enter the coelomic cavity by removing one flank.

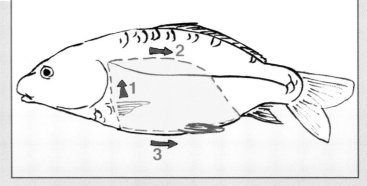

► Fig 2.8 Diagram showing sequence and direction of incisions to remove flank.

and bottom to allow its removal (Fig 2.6). These can now be examined under a light microscope for the presence of gill parasites such as *Dactylogyrus* (5.8.3) or to check for any obvious pathology of the gill filaments and lamellae. Samples can be submitted for histopathological examination.

Before examining the coelomic (body) cavity, the external surfaces should be sterilised to reduce the risk of introducing contamination. This is best achieved by dipping in or applying 70% alcohol (surgical spirit) to the outside of the fish. The fish is then laid on its side on a non-slip surface.

Using a sterile pair of fine scissors and forceps three incisions are made (Figs 2.7 and 2.8).

The first starts at the ventral mid-line just caudal to the pectoral fin and moves dorsally (upwards) to the level of the spine, paralleling the operculum (gill cover).

▲ Fig 2.9 Identify the main structures and assess any abnormalities.

▼ Fig 2.10 Annotated diagram of Fig 2.9.

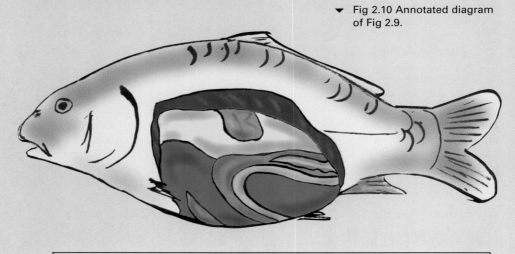

■ Muscle		▪ Gonad (undeveloped/quiescent)	
■ Kidney		▪ Hepatopancreas	
■ Swimbladder		▪ Gut	

The second starts at the most dorsal point of the first incision and follows the contours of the body cavity parallel to the spinal column before curving ventrally (downwards) to the anus.

The third cut is midline along the belly of the fish again to the anus, thereby connecting the other two incisions. This should allow the wall of the coelomic cavity to be removed.

Assess the type and character of any coelomic fluid present and collect with a sterile syringe and needle if required. Watch out for any adhesions (areas of attachment) of organs to the inside surface of the body cavity as these may be due to areas of inflammation. However it is normal in koi (and goldfish) for there to be a degree of adhesion present between the internal organs. Most of the internal organs should now be exposed.

One should now set about identifying the main structures (Figs 2.9; 2.10; 2.11 and 2.12):-

The swimbladder is a large, silvery organ lying along the dorsal boundary of the coelomic cavity. In koi it is divided into an anterior section and a posterior chamber. These are continuous, although the anterior section is less expansible. Immediately dorsal to the swimbladder lie the dark red kidneys that lie, strap-like, over the middle of the swimbladder and immediately below it and lateral are the gonads. The kidneys are divided into cranial (anterior) and caudal halves. The caudal part overlies the swimbladder; the cranial part is immediately cranial to the anterior section of the swimbladder.

Koi have no distinct, glandular stomach or pyloric caecae. They maintain a digestive tract at a pH higher than those fish with stomachs and they have associated enzyme adaptations, such that optimum protease and amylase occurs over a wide pH range. The intestines are usually very obvious ventrally, although in large koi they may be partially obscured by fat and the hepatopancreas. The spleen is often hidden within the intestinal mass.

The liver, or more correctly the hepatopancreas, occupies the anterior border of the coelomic cavity and is a sizable organ. Usually a deep red, its colour can vary markedly depending upon factors such as fatty diet or vitellogenesis. In koi there is no separate pancreas, instead pancreatic cells are distributed throughout the hepatic tissue, hence this combined organ is known as the hepatopancreas.

The heart lies immediately anterior to the liver, often at the level of and between the pectoral fins (pectoral girdle) and is separated from the main coelomic cavity by a thick membrane (the pericardium).

◀ Fig 2.11 Body cavity of a mature koi, showing developed gonad (testis in this case). Note the more normal colour of the hepatopancreas.

▼ Fig 2.12 Annotated diagram of Fig 2.11.

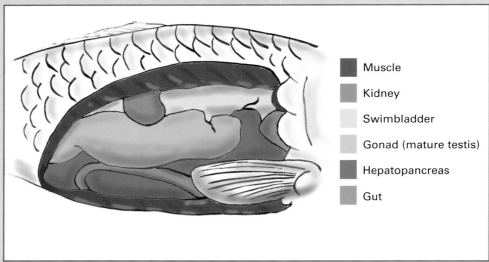

█ Muscle

█ Kidney

█ Swimbladder

█ Gonad (mature testis)

█ Hepatopancreas

█ Gut

▶ Fig 2.13 Remove the gastro-intestinal tract including the hepatopancreas. The pneumatic duct connecting the swimbladder with the oesophagus can be identified and examined, before resecting to allow removal of the guts.

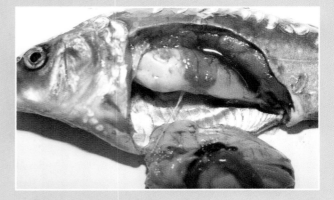

34

◀ Fig 2.14 Examine the hepatopancreas, gall bladder and spleen. Fatty livers such as this one will often break down during handling.

▼ Fig 2.15 Annotated diagram of Fig 2.14.

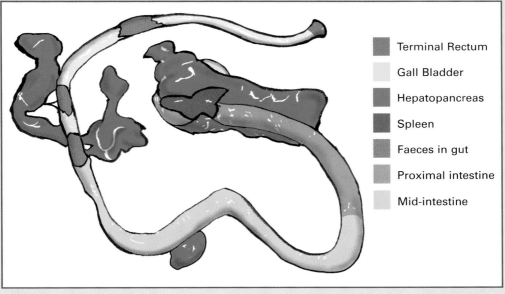

- Terminal Rectum
- Gall Bladder
- Hepatopancreas
- Spleen
- Faeces in gut
- Proximal intestine
- Mid-intestine

Having assessed the internal organs for any obvious abnormality, either physical or positional, then the whole of the gastrointestinal tract is removed (including the hepatopancreas) (Fig 2.13). This is achieved by cutting through the oesophagus proximally, and through the rectum as close to the anus as possible distally. If there is a risk of escape of gut contents then these should be tied off prior to removal. Koi have a direct connection between the swimbladder and the oesophagus (carp are physostomes). This connection is called the pneumatic duct and with care can be identified. Look for any abnormalities or blockages before resecting this.

◀ Fig 2.16 Remove the
gonads and examine.

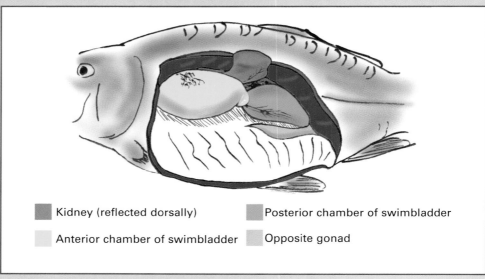

Kidney (reflected dorsally)   Posterior chamber of swimbladder

Anterior chamber of swimbladder   Opposite gonad

▲ Fig 2.17 Annotated diagram
of Fig 2.16.

▶ Fig 2.18 Remove the
swimbladder and examine.

◀ Fig 2.19 If appropriate, remove a section of the kidney for touch preparations.

▶ Fig 2.20 Make a dorsal wedge, involving kidney tissue, dorsal musculature and spinal column.

▼ Fig 2.21 Annotated diagram of Fig 2.20.

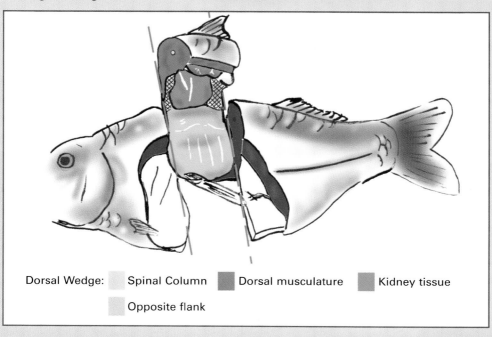

Dorsal Wedge: Spinal Column   Dorsal musculature   Kidney tissue

Opposite flank

◀ Fig 2.22 Cut through pericardium and examine heart.

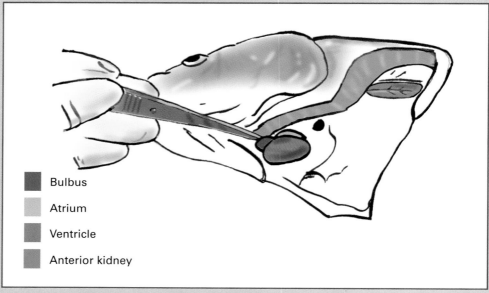

Bulbus

Atrium

Ventricle

Anterior kidney

▲ (Above and Right)
Fig 2.23 Annotated diagram of Fig 2.22, plus schematic diagram of koi heart showing associated structures.

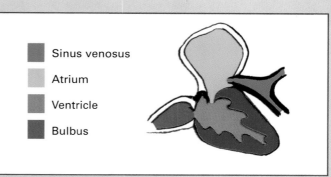

Sinus venosus

Atrium

Ventricle

Bulbus

◄ Fig 2.24 Cut into muscle blocks.

▼ (Below Left) Fig 2.25 Remove the eyes. This illustrates a whole eye, plus the completely spherical lens removed from the other eye.

(Below Right) Fig 2.26 Examination of the brain is difficult because it is so delicate and easily damaged.

▼ Fig 2.27 Examine the entire gastro-intestinal tract.

▲ Fig 2.28
Severe Chilonodella infestation – note the excessive mucus production.

▼ Fig 2.29
The small lesion on the operculum of this koi is
Dermocsytidium koi.

Assess the visible surfaces of the whole gastrointestinal tract (Figs 2.14 and 2.15). Hepatic tissue is usually a dark red/tan colour, although its colour can vary. The edges of the hepatopancreas are often indistinct. Several incisions should be made into the substance of the hepatopancreas to examine for parasites or obvious lesions. Any discoloured or raised areas should be retained for histopathology (see later).

Associated with the liver tissue is the gallbladder. This contains bile, which is usually a yellow to dark green colour. Fish that have been dead a while may show staining of the surrounding tissues with bile. If the fish has not fed for some time the gallbladder may be quite distended. The bile can be collected with a syringe for examination for protozoa or frozen for toxicological analysis.

The spleen is a flat, triangular dark red organ. However it may not be immediately obvious as it is often hidden in fat or by loops of gut. If the spleen is obviously swollen it should be cultured, or touch preparations performed (see later).

The guts are separated out from the hepatopancreas and placed to one side to reduce the risk of accidental contamination of the other organs.

Returning to the coelomic cavity the sex organs should now be removed (Fig 2.16). Fish that are not sexually active may have insignificant gonads. As a general rule immature but developing eggs are greenish or whitish, whilst mature eggs are yellow. Brown, black and obviously degenerating eggs can be a sign of egg retention. Mature testes in males are usually large, firm and white. Smearing the cut surface of testes on to a slide may help one to gain an idea of sperm motility.

The swimbladder should now be examined (Figs 2.16, 2.17 and 2.18). There are retia mirabilia which are an often circular patch(es) of blood vessels on the surface of the caudal chambers of the swimbladder. Look for any signs of haemorrhage on the surface, or exudates inside one or more chambers.

The caudal kidneys can be removed next. These are important, as bacteria tend to localise here in large numbers in cases of septicaemia. Touch preparations (Fig 2.19) and bacterial culture are recommended. Unfortunately the kidneys are often easily damaged and so, for histopathology, a dorsal wedge is taken (Figs 2.20 and 2.21). This involves taking a section of kidney, spinal column and dorsal musculature by incising dorsally from the abdomen up towards the back of the fish. A piece of the anterior kidney can be taken as well.

The heart can now be examined (Figs 2.22 and 2.23). Look for an increased amount of fluid around the heart, as well as any obvious lesions, haemorrhages or raised areas. Sever the cranial and caudal connections. If the heart is large then incise along its length to examine the internal surface and the valves.

Several incisions should be made into the muscle blocks of the fish to look for lesions such as parasitic metacercaria (Fig 2.24). Examine the colour and texture of the muscle, especially for any signs of wasting.

Skin samples can be taken for histopathology if required. If there is an obvious skin lesion such as an ulcer then make sure to include some healthy normal tissue surrounding it in the sample. Also try to submit samples which include sections of the lateral line.

The eyes can now be removed and examined (Fig 2.25). Remove each eye and either submit it for histopathology whole or incise into it – it will tend to collapse but it will allow one to visualise abnormalities of the lens.

If the fish has shown nervous signs or it is otherwise felt necessary to examine the brain, this can be done by removing a section of the skull immediately above the eyes (Fig 2.26). The brain is easily damaged during this process. Ideally, remove the head/skull from the rest of the body and make small holes into the skull cavity before placing the whole into formal saline. In this way the brain is preserved and firmed by the preservative and can either be subsequently easily removed, or sectioned in situ. The brain deteriorates very quickly so its examination is only suitable in very fresh specimens.

Now return to the guts. Examine for any abnormalities such as raised areas or haemorrhages on the outside (serosal) surface. The entire length of the bowel is opened and examined for parasites and obvious lesions (Fig 2.27). If food is present try to identify it. Sections from all parts of the intestine and colon should be submitted for histopathology.

2.3.1 Sample collection

i) Viral. If virus isolation is required, then transfer of sample tissue to an appropriate Viral Transport Media and store at around 4°C.

ii) Bacterial. Bacteriological samples can be taken either with swabs or sterile loops. The external surface of the organ is first seared, then an incision is made into the organ with a sterile scalpel blade or scissors. The loop/swab is introduced. If samples are to be forwarded to laboratories, then Bacterial Transport Media is recommended. Some bacteria are difficult to culture routinely eg. *Mycobacteria*. These are more likely to be diagnosed from histopathological sections or needle aspirates, with special staining techniques.

iii) Chlamydial. Suspect samples should be transferred to a suitable Chlamydial transport medium. *Chlamydia* can be demonstrated with histopathology.

iv) Fungal. Same principles as for Bacterial samples. Some fungi eg. *Ichthyophonus* are diagnosed primarily with histopathology.

v) Parasitic.
a) Macroparasites eg. Helminths, can be teased free and removed in toto, or with part of the organ at the point of attachment.
b) Microparasites eg. Protozoa. Best diagnosed in situ with histopathology eg. *Hoferellus cyprinii*.

vi) Histopathology. Sections of tissue are preserved in formal saline as a fixative for histopathological examination. In all cases try to include some adjacent healthy tissue in the sample taken. Relatively small pieces are more than adequate for the majority of samples. Care should be taken to ensure samples are placed into relatively large volumes of formal saline (roughly 1:10). If brain is to be preserved, then open the skull to allow the fixative access.

vii) Touch Preparations. Samples of tissues have a cut surface briefly dabbed on to a clean glass slide. These slides are then stained and examined microscopically. This technique gives information on cell types present and certain pathogens eg. bacteria (although this is of very little use in identifying the species of bacteria).

viii) Toxicology. Samples required and how they are to be handled vary with which toxin one is looking for. Therefore I would advise that you discuss what you require with the laboratory first.

Chapter Three

Anaesthesia and Clinical Procedures

3.1.1 Anaesthesia

If one is working with koi, at some point there will be a need to sedate or anaesthetise a fish as part of its health management, such as to treat an ulcer. When anaesthetising fish, always have a bath of well aerated water ready for recovery. This should be of the same temperature and water quality of the water in which the fish is anaesthetised.

3.1.2 Stages of anaesthesia

TABLE 2

Stage	Category	Response seen in Fish	Comments
0	Normal	Swimming actively and responding to stimuli. Good equilibrium and normal muscle tone.	
I	Light sedation	Continues to swim with normal equilibrium and muscle tone. Respiration normal. Slight loss of reaction to external stimuli.	
I	Light narcosis	There may be a brief excitement phase. There is an increase in the respiratory rate, some loss of equilibrium that the fish will try to correct. The koi will attempt to correct manual repositioning. There is a loss of muscle tone.	
II	Deep Narcosis	There is a total loss of equilibrium and a failure to correct if repositioned. The respiratory rate reduces to near normal. There is further decrease in muscle tone but still some reaction to strong external stimuli.	Suitable for skin scrapes, gill and fin biopsies, ulcer treatment.

Continued |

III	Light Anaesthesia	Total loss of muscle tone and responds only to deep pressure. The respiratory rate is further depressed.	Suitable for minor surgery.
III	Deep Anaesthesia	Complete loss of reactivity. Respiratory rate is very low and the heart rate is slow.	Suitable for major surgery.
IV	Medullary Collapse	Total loss of opercular movement, followed several minutes later by cardiac arrest.	

3.1.3 Benzocaine

The most commonly used fish anaesthetic. It is a white crystalline powder insoluble in water. It must first be dissolved in either ethanol or acetone, both of which can be irritant to the fish, and in the case of ethanol may have a slight sedative effect in its own right. A higher dosage is required in warmer water, possibly due to improved metabolism of the drug. However it is more toxic at higher temperatures. It is fat-soluble so larger fish or females with roe will absorb greater quantities than leaner fish. This increases the risk of medullary collapse in these fish, and may produce a prolonged recovery phase. There is a build up of lactic acid during anaesthesia with benzocaine – it is unclear whether this is a direct hypoxic effect or due to a reduced respiratory rate, so the anaesthetic bath and the recovery bath should be well aerated.

Dose: Make up a stock solution of 100g of benzocaine to one litre of ethanol or acetone. This is then added to the anaesthetic bath with the fish in situ until effect is seen.

3.1.4 MS222

This is tricaine methane sulphonate, and is a highly water-soluble analogue of benzocaine. In solution methane sulphonic acid is formed which causes a marked drop in pH of the solution. If the powder is dropped incrementally directly into the water the fish may show escape responses due to the sudden fall in pH. A better method is to make a stock solution buffered with sodium bicarbonate. It has the same hypoxic effects as benzocaine.

Dose: First make a saturated solution of sodium bicarbonate – this will stabilise the pH to around 7.0 to 7.5. The stock solution of MS222 is a 10g/l of this solution. Add incrementally to effect, or start with a 50mg/l solution i.e. add 5ml of the 10g/l solution per litre of water in the immersion bath. Increase as required.

3.1.5 Oil of Cloves

Becoming popular amongst hobbyists, it is normally used for its local anaesthetic properties but it can act as a fish anaesthetic. There appears to be no particular dose rate and there is a varied susceptibility between individual koi, which is not size dependant. Although not considered water-soluble, there must be some solution of active compounds to explain its effect.

Dose: 1ml of clove oil into two gallons of water in a bag. This is shaken vigorously, and left for five to ten minutes with the bag sealed as tightly as possible. This provides your anaesthetic solution. Add incrementally to effect.

3.1.6 Recovery

Once the anaesthetic procedure is completed, the koi is replaced into a well-aerated recovery bath. This should contain water of the same temperature and quality as that used for anaesthetic induction. With gentle digital pressure keep the mouth open and move the fish forward through the water such that water is allowed to pass over the gills and out through the operculae. Try not to swish the koi backwards and forwards through the water, as water passing backwards over the gill lamellae can cause damage to these delicate structures as well as reversing the normal countercurrent gaseous exchange system which could reduce the koi's oxygen uptake.

3.1.7 Dopram-V Oral Drops (Fort Dodge)

Doxapram hydrochloride is a respiratory stimulant designed to cross mucous membranes. In practice it appears to work well as an aid to anaesthetic recovery if applied to the inside of the mouth. Overuse can cause a hyperventilation with an increased oxygen demand such that a hypoxia may result, so make sure water is well aerated. Dopram-V Oral Drops are not licensed for use in koi in the UK (see 3.2.7).

3.2.1 Medicine administration

3.2.2 Injection sites

Most koi, barring very small specimens, can be injected. I prefer to inject midline immediately in front of the dorsal fin between the muscle blocks. Take care to insert the needle beneath any scales and not through them. The epaxial muscles are well-developed in koi and using a 23G or 25G needle presents no problem. Absorption is good and there is little chance of any drug being squeezed back out due to muscle action. Unfortunately if there is an injection-site reaction this is the most visible place on the entire fish as seen from above. If the fish is large and one is concerned, then the injection can be given immediately behind the dorsal fin. Some people inject into the muscle at the base of the pectoral fins. This muscle is well vascularised so drug uptake is good. This is fine in large koi but a problem in smaller fish. Injections into the tail and flank muscles are not to be recommended on two counts:-

i) First the arrangement of the muscle blocks means that the drugs tend to be squeezed out of the injection site as the fish swims off.

ii) Carp have a partial renal portal system whereby a significant amount of the venous drainage from the caudal part of the body passes through the kidneys first before being diluted in the general circulation. Since some antibiotics can damage the kidney tissues at high concentrations I do not recommend this route. Intra-coelomic injections are best avoided as the internal organs are tightly adhered together, so there is a high risk of accidental organ puncture.

Intra-venous injections can be given into the ventral caudal vein or medial opercular vein. The ventral caudal vein is accessed by inserting the needle ventrally in the midline and advancing it until bone is reached. It is then drawn back slightly until blood is seen in the hub of the needle. This is also a suitable site for taking blood samples.

3.2.3 Antibiotic impregnated foods
These are available on veterinary prescription in the UK. These foods are presented either as flake or as sinking pellets.

Unfortunately most koi are fed on floating pellets, and appear not to recognise sinking pellets as food. Ideal for feeding to in contact fish that may be at risk, they are useless if the affected fish are showing appetite loss. As a rough guide, feed to 1% bodyweight.

The drug of choice, if only available as a powder or tablet form, can be administered to koi with food as follows:-

i)   Crush tablets, and mix powder with a small amount of vegetable oil into a paste.
ii) Mix this paste with an appropriate amount of pelleted food.
iii) Allow to air dry before feeding.

3.2.4 Bath
Allows accurate dosing but there is the stress of capture and a risk of poor water quality.

3.2.5 In situ i.e. into the pond or aquarium
The easy option but antibacterials may destroy biological filtration. Other disadvantages include risk of inaccurate dosage and expense due to large volumes of water that may require treatment. Also, drugs in solution are constantly being deactivated by reducing substances, pH and chelation and therefore have variable and unpredictable half-lives

3.2.6 Gavage
One can give an accurate dosage but there may be variable gut absorption as well as the stress of handling.

Use a Jackson Cat catheter or some other round-ended pliable tube with holes at the side.

3.2.7 Drug dosages

A wide range of therapeutic drugs can be used but no Prescription Only Medicines (PoM) are specifically licensed in the UK for use in koi. The dose rates for the majority of these are discussed under the relevant disease heading. Choice of antibiotic will depend upon bacterial sensitivity, but here are some that may prove useful. Wherever possible choose a bacteriocidal (BC) antibiotic rather than a bacteriostatic (BS) one as it cannot be assumed that the koi immune system will be fully functional.

Enrofloxacin (BC)
a) Injection: 5-10mg.kg every 48 hours for 15 days
b) Bath: 2.5mg/l as a five hour bath every 24 hours for 5-7 days
c) Infeed: 5mg/kg daily for 10-14 days

Marbofloxacin (BC)
a) Injection 5mg/kg every 7 days

Potentiated sulphonamides such as sulfadiazine/trimethoprim combinations (BC).
a) Injection: 30mg/kg every 24 hours for 7-10 days
b) Infeed: 30mg/kg every 24 hrs for 10-14 days

Oxolinic Acid
a) Infeed: 10mg/kg daily for 10 days

Oxytetracycline (BS)
a) Injection: 10mg/kg daily for 10-14 days
b) Bath: 100mg/l for one hour daily for 5-10 days
c) Infeed: 75mg/kg daily for 7-14 days
NB: Oxytetracycline is chelated by hard water so dosages must be adjusted. Used extensively over the years there is much resistance around and at higher dose rates e.g. 40mg/kg by injection it may be immunosuppressive.

Metronidazole (BC)
a) Bath: <50mg/l daily for up to 24hrs for 10 days
b) Infeed: 0.3% (200mg/100g of food) daily for 10 days
Metronidazole can be used to treat protozoan infestations as well as metronidazole-sensitive bacterial infections.

3.2.8 Proprietary medicines

Producing off-the-shelf medicines for ornamental fish is big business, but very few hold a marketing authorisation. Many of them are very good, especially the ectoparasitic medications, and it is recommended that they be used initially for these problems. Many however appear to be not so good. True to say that some of this could be down to misdiagnosis by the hobbyist, but even so they should be used with caution and according to the manufacturers recommendations. Always make an attempt at diagnosis first. Unfortunately many proprietary medications are poor and claims are made which can neither be substantiated nor proven in practice.

3.3.1 Radiography

Koi can be radiographed. It is essential to produce high quality radiographs if one is to use radiography as a diagnostic tool. The following recommendations will help to produce diagnostically useful radiographs:-

Anaesthetise or sedate the koi (see 3.1.1). Radiographing koi in situ using perspex aquaria can be done, but the exposure factors become unnecessarily high, being governed by depth of water to be penetrated rather than the size of the fish. Also there is a high likelihood of movement blur of the resulting radiographic images.

Care should be taken to prevent water entering the cassettes during radiography – they can be placed in clear plastic bags if necessary.

Use rare earth green emitting screens with single sided green emulsion. This produces an image of high definition and improves the quality of fine details such as the pharyngeal teeth. As the film only has emulsion on one side, exposure factors will need to be increased in comparison to those used for double sided film. The speed of the latter is often so fast, that for radiographing small specimens very low exposure factors are needed. This can produce deterioration in image quality.

To produce a sharp image cone down the exposed area as much as possible.

Lateral View – This is the most useful view (See Figs 3.1 and 3.2). Position the body of the koi as parallel as possible to the film to prevent any rotational distortion of the radiographic image. This view is ideal for assessing swimbladder disorders and skeletal defects. In addition the swimbladder provides a point of reference, for instance it will be displaced ventrally by enlargement of one or both kidneys.

Dorso-Ventral View – This is of limited value due to superimposition of structures such as the vertebrae, ribs and skull bones (See Figs 3.3 and 3.4). However it is useful to evaluate spinal curvature or damage, or lateral displacement of the swimbladder by coelomic neoplasia. Remember to label Right/Left sides.

3.4.1 Euthanasia

In principle the method of euthanasia should be stress free and render the fish immediately insensible. In practice, handling of the fish is always required which will inevitably cause stress. The method of euthanasia should also take into account whether a post mortem is to be done.

3.4.2 Recommended methods

These include overdosing with anaesthetic such as MS222 or benzocaine.

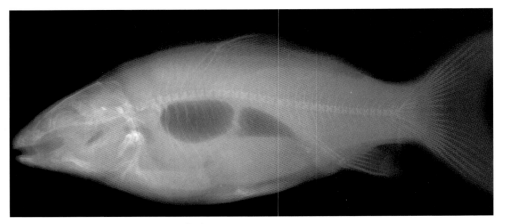

▲ Fig 3.1 Lateral view of a koi.

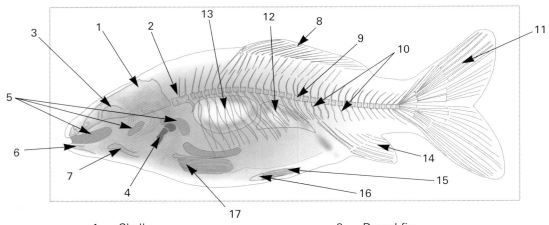

1	Skull	8	Dorsal fin
2	Weberian apparatus	9	Vertebrae
3	Orbit	10	Ribs
4	Pharyngeal teeth	11	Caudal fin
5	Air in pharynx	12	Swimbladder (posterior chamber)
6	Lower jaw	13	Swimbladder (anterior chamber)
7	Preoperculum bone	14	Anal fin
		15	Pelvic fin
		16	Pelvic bone
		17	Pectoral fin

▲ Fig 3.2 Annotated diagram of Fig 3.1.

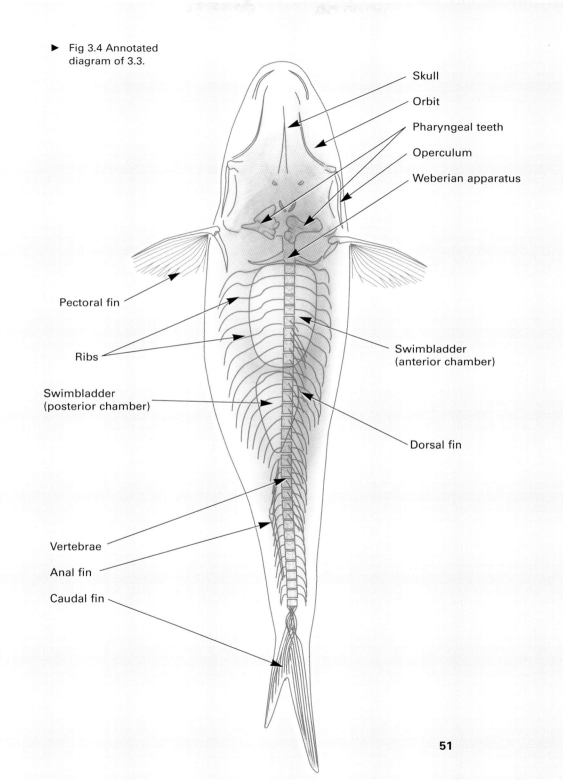

► Fig 3.4 Annotated diagram of 3.3.

Skull

Orbit

Pharyngeal teeth

Operculum

Weberian apparatus

Pectoral fin

Ribs

Swimbladder
(anterior chamber)

Swimbladder
(posterior chamber)

Dorsal fin

Vertebrae

Anal fin

Caudal fin

51

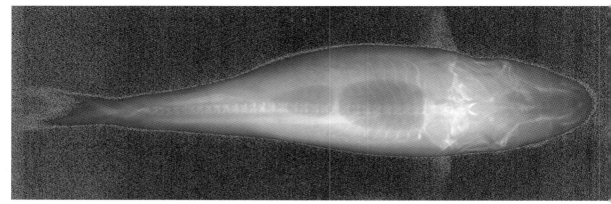

▲ Fig 3.3 Dorso-ventral view of koi.

Alternatively, with larger fish, pentobarbitone can be administered intravenously into the ventral tail vein (see 3.2.1) In an emergency small fish can be overdosed with Alka-Seltzer – the massive release of carbonic acid as the tablets dissolve will anaesthetise the fish. An unsightly scum is left on the surface of the water. Stunning with an angler's priest or another blunt instrument should render the fish insensible, and this can be followed by decapitation.

3.4.3 Methods of euthanasia to avoid
These include decapitation without prior stunning. Fish nerve tissue is tolerant of anoxia and the brain may continue to function for some time after decapitation. Freezing is a method in favour with many hobbyists, but koi are able to cope with very low temperatures (see 1.1.3) and the mechanism of death by hypothermia is described in 1.1.4. Remember that just because a fish cannot respond to a stimulus when hypothermic does not guarantee that it cannot perceive it.

3.5.1 Minor Surgical Procedures
Included here are a couple of minor surgical procedures. No details of intra-coelomic surgery are given here, as it should only be attempted by skilled professionals such as veterinary surgeons. There is no excuse for undertaking heroic surgery on the kitchen table – indeed in the UK one may leave oneself open to prosecution under the Protection Of Animals Act 1911 for cruelty and causing unnecessary suffering.

3.5.2 Suturing Split Fins

Pectoral fins and dorsal fins in particular may split or be torn between the rays. Usually these heal without any difficulty, but occasionally the split continues all the way to the base of the fin. Such tears may not heal well, and so placing a few simple interrupted sutures across two or three rays on either side will appose the edges of the tear to allow normal healing to occur (Fig 3.5). Use 4/0 Vicryl (Ethicon) with a round bodied needle by preference, and either allow the sutures to degrade naturally or remove once healing is advanced.

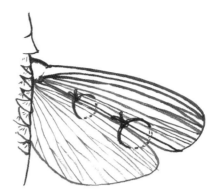

▲ Fig 3.5 Suturing a split pectoral fin.

3.5.3 Removal of Small Cutaneous Masses

Small, non-invasive growths and tumours of the skin can be removed with care. With the koi anaesthetised, sterilise the area with a proprietary iodine compound such as Tamedine (Vetark). Using a sterile No15 scalpel blade the growth is readily removed (Fig 3.6). Koi skin is very inelastic so it is very unlikely that the deficit can be closed with suture material or tissue glue, so one must treat the surgical site as one would a small ulcer (see 5.4.4).

▲ Fig 3.6 Surgical removal of a cutaneous mass.

Chapter Four

Diseases and Disorders of Eggs and Fry

4.1.1 Broodstock

The preparation of broodstock is often overlooked. A thorough physical examination early in the season is important, taking care to check for any signs of ulceration, or parasites. Remember to check underneath the fish, as lesions on the belly and anal fin can easily be overlooked. Correct feeding is important, as both sexes require extra protein for normal ovarian/testicular growth and function. Fats are also important, with significant reserves being laid down in the liver. These are utilised for energy during spawning and, in females, are needed for egg production. Therefore, diets with at least 8% lipids (fats) and 35-40% high quality protein should be provided. Failure to provide this may result in broodfish with reduced spawning vigour reduced fertility and poor hatching.

Breeding males may produce a mass of small dermal nodules, called nuptial tubercles, on the operculae and the leading edge of the pectoral fins. Beware mistakenly diagnosing these as pathological.

4.1.2 Care of eggs

Once released into the water, a koi egg must be fertilised within 30-60 seconds (sperm remain viable for 1-2 minutes). Often, up to 40% of a spawning can be infertile. To try to reduce this, use at least two males to each female during spawning.

Following spawning, the eggs absorb water and swell, in a process called hardening. This is achieved by osmosis, water entering the relatively concentrated egg from the dilute surrounding medium.

In waters which are excessively hard, with high levels of dissolved salts (such as certain spring waters), the difference in the levels of dissolved substances in the egg, compared with the surrounding water, may not be sufficient to induce osmosis and, hence, normal hardening.

Other causes of egg mortality and low hatchability include:

i) Low oxygen levels.

ii) Incorrect water temperature. Fatal below around 16°C; above 25°C – stimulates development but may produce weakened and deformed fry; over 30°C – usually rapidly fatal. Rapid temperature changes will also cause embryonic death.

Bacterial and fungal diseases can also cause serious mortality of eggs and newly hatched fry.

Control: Fungal infections of eggs Malachite Green, either as a bath at 5.0mg/l for 60 minutes, or 0.2mg/l as a continuous bath.

Bacterial Infections of eggs: Antibiotic required (varies). Erythromycin at 50mg/l is absorbed across the eggshell.

4.1.3 Care of fry

After around two to six days (depending upon the ambient water temperature), the fry hatch out. At this stage, they show marked light avoidance, seeking darkened areas in which to lie to absorb their yolk sac.

After 48 to 72 hours, fry development has progressed to the stage where they can become free-swimming. Following a quick dash to the surface to take in a gulp of atmospheric air which is forced into the swimbladder, the fry alter their behaviour and seek out light, which usually draws them towards the highest densities of their food – microscopic algae and animals called infusoria. Factors to consider are:-

i) Excessive levels of illumination or inadequate provision of shaded areas in the first two to three days can be stressful to fry, possibly opening the way to secondary infections.

ii) Very high or low temperatures are also stressful and, if uncorrected, may cause fatalities. This is also true of rapid temperature fluctuations. Further, growing on fry at too high a temperature can cause a loss in colour.

iii) Following hatching, the oxygen requirements of the fry increase dramatically and, again, as the fry become free-swimming. Factors that further exacerbate this demand are high temperatures, high stocking densities, and overfeeding.

iv) Poor water quality can also cause a loss of fry, especially high ammonia and nitrite levels. Some poor waters may have a thick, proteinaceous film at the surface, making it difficult for the fry to take in air into their swimbladder.

v) Gross overcrowding of the fry will lead to stunting. Koi closest to the original wild carp can grow at a prodigious rate, and can often out-compete their brothers and sisters for food, and if the size differential is too great, then cannibalism may result.

vi) On the subject of food, fry growth can also be reduced by feeding insufficient or poor-quality foods lacking in essential amino acids such as arginine and valine.

vii) Young fry do not possess a fully functioning immune system and this, combined with a rather delicate constitution, means that they are susceptible to a wide range of diseases. Many bacterial and fungal diseases can attack these young koi.

Treatment: Fungal and bacterial infections of fry – Where appropriate, treat as for adults.

4.2.1 Some notable parasitic infections include:

4.2.2 *Icthyobodo (Costia) necator* which attacks the eggs and subsequently any carp fry which hatch. Overcrowding and high temperatures can cause explosive increases in Icthyobodo, resulting in mass fry mortality.
Treatment: Use proprietary ectoparasitic medication.

4.2.3 *Sphaerosphora renicola*
Uncommon in the UK, this myxosporean parasite is the cause of Swimbladder Inflammation (SBI) in carp fry which can present as balance problems and inappetance (loss of appetite). At high temperatures (25 to 30°C) the signs of SBI increase, with associated mortality.

Should the carp survive to the following year, they may then show vague signs, including anaemia (pale gills) and kidney enlargement. Secondary bacterial infections of the swimbladder are common, with one or both chambers filling with pus-like material, and gross thickening of the swimbladder wall.
Treatment: There is no recognised treatment but Fumigillin at 1g/kg food for 10-14 days has been used for prevention.

4.2.4 *Bothriocephalus*
As the fry grow, they change their feeding habits to include small crustacea, including *Daphnia* and copepods. This can expose them to certain worm infestations, such as *Bothriocephalus* which uses a copepod as an intermediate host.
Treatment: Praziquantel at 10mg/l for 3 hours at 22°C.

4.2.5 Predators
In a pond situation, or if one is using live food, one should carefully monitor for the presence of predators, such as the voracious dragonfly larvae or the anemone-like *Hydra*.
Control: Predators such as Hydra and dragonfly larvae. In water treatments are fatal to fry, therefore attempt to control by screening all introduced plants. Control in large ponds is not feasible.

Chapter Five

Infectious Diseases of Koi

5.1.1 Immune System

Most pathogens of Koi are normally found in small numbers, both on the fish and in the environment. This constant low challenge helps to keep the immune system of the fish primed, as a kind of natural vaccination. The immune system of koi can be said to comprise of two interrelated parts:-

5.1.2 Non-specific

This comprises primarily of the skin, which acts as a physical and osmotic barrier between the fish and the surrounding watery environment. Present on the epidermis is the cuticle, a mucopolysaccharide layer around 1.0 mm thick. This is largely secreted by the epidermal cells, although it also contains mucus produced by the goblet cells (See diagrammatic section through koi skin, page 94-95). Contained in this layer is lysozyme (a non-specific antibacterial enzyme) and free fatty acids (believed to be antibacterial), sloughed cells and specific immunoglobulins (antibodies).

5.1.3 Specific

This comprises of :- Humoral immunity. This consists of antibody production – the protein compounds that recognise and latch on to pathogens to allow their subsequent destruction by specialised cells or complement. Immunoglobulins are produced by specific white blood cells (B-lymphocytes) and most of this activity takes place in the haematopoetic tissues of the cranial (anterior) pole of the kidney, rather than the spleen.

There is a reduction in antibody producing lymphocytes at temperatures over 28°C, so it would seem that the ability of a koi to fight off a disease challenge might be inhibited at temperatures below 18°C or above 28°C. This fits in well with the PBT of koi (22 – 28°C). At temperatures of 18-28°C antibody production is at its best, with antibodies appearing in the blood roughly 7-11 days after challenge by infection. There is a very good memory response, whereby if a koi has already been exposed to a particular bacteria and produced antibodies to it and is then presented with a second challenge of the same bacteria there is a quicker response (4 days) plus higher levels of antibody. This would be typical of the situation in late spring, summer and early autumn in the UK. If carp are infected at a time of high temperature, but the temperature then drops to around 10 – 12°C within 7 days, antibodies will be produced but at a much slower rate. This situation mimics what we find in autumn or early spring where warmer periods alternate with colder snaps.

At temperatures below 12-18°C there is no memory response, so it may be that the formation of memory cells may be a temperature sensitive process. Carp which are experiencing bacterial challenge at low temperatures will not produce antibodies so long as they are kept at these temperatures. Subsequently raising the water temperature will trigger an antibody production but it will take longer and antibody levels are lower. This would be the situation in koi exposed to infection during the winter and early spring. If carp are exposed to a very small bacterial challenge at low temperatures, some of them can become immunotolerant. This means that they will fail to recognise this particular bacteria as a pathogen and will not mount any sort of immune response, even if the water warms up to optimum of 18-25°C.

Taken a step further, this could mean that these fish can become carriers of a particular bacterium and will act as a continuous source of infection to other koi without showing any signs of disease themselves.

5.1.4 Cellular immunity

This contains the groups of white blood cells (T-lymphocytes) that directly ingest pathogens such as bacteria such as heterophils, eosinophils and macrophages. Heterophils are the first white blood cells to invade the site of an injury, whilst the numbers of macrophages increases to a peak at around ten days. Macrophages not only ingest bacteria but also damaged tissue fragments as part of the "clean-up" operation. Temperature again appears important. At a temperature of 32°C there is a weaker response in T-lymphocytes to mitogen challenge than at 28°C, and 28°C appears to give a maximal proliferation of T-lymphocytes experimentally, above that of either 25°C or 32°C. Therefore, in the majority of cases it would seem to benefit sick koi to keep them at the higher end of their PBT at around 28°C. This, in effect, mimics a behavioural fever (see 1.1.4).

As part of the immune response, changes can be seen in the blood that in the future may be able to be used diagnostically. In healthy carp, heterophils, monocytes and eosinophils appear to be rare. Each of these constitute around 1% of total White Blood cell Count (WBC), whilst lymphocytes consist of around 90% WBC. Obtaining a blood sample (see 4.2.1) and staining a smear (with Diff-Quick or Leishman's stain for example) may be of use. In addition to demonstrating blood parasites, such smears may be useful in diagnosing :-

Bacterial infections – there is an increase in heterophils (heterophilia), aneosinophila and a fall in lymphocytes (lymphopaenia).

Protozoal infestations – heterophilia with a left shift, plus lymphopaenia. Late in the course of the disease, an increase in basophils is seen.

Dactylogyrus infestations – heterophilia and an increase in monocytes (monocytosis). Stress – heterophilia and lymphopaenia. There is also an increase in the Packed Cell Volume (PCV) from a normal of around 32-35 l/l. This increase in PCV is thought to be due to erythrocyte swelling, release of stored erythrocytes from the spleen and loss of water from the vasculature.

5.2.1
One of the most important factors in the aetiology of many koi diseases is stress, due to inappropriate husbandry, poor water quality and so on. Another stressor is poor capture technique.

5.2.2 Stress hormones
Koi tend to be kept in large, deep ponds so that trying to catch the fish often proves virtually impossible. The fish you are after darts away from the net just when you think you've caught it, careering off into the side of the pond whilst the rest of the fish panic, forming into a tight school shooting from one end of the pond to the other. Eventually, the target fish is caught either by a stroke of luck or when it gives in to sheer exhaustion.

The fish can see the incoming net and, with its lateral line, will sense the pressure wave produced. This is likely to initiate an escape response, accompanied by a sudden surge of the flight or fight hormones - adrenaline and noradrenaline -from the chromaffin tissue (fish do not have adrenal glands as such). In handled trout these hormones can surge up to one hundred times the normal value in the blood, causing an increase in heart rate, dilatation of the blood vessels in the gills and constriction of those vessels in the main body; there is a fall in blood glucose and an alteration in the gill ion permeability therefore affecting osmoregulation. The interrenal glands also produce large quantities of the natural steroid cortisol. Although this helps the koi to cope physiologically with the stress, it too alters the gill ionic and water permeability.

Many koi will appear to haemorrhage from the gills following capture as a sign of stress. Whether this is a true haemorrhage, or a diapodesis, is uncertain but it is likely that this is due to the effects of endogenous cortisol on the gills. Cortisol is also immunosuppressive, especially if the fish is subjected to this at frequent intervals such as in a dealer's pond.

5.2.3 C-start reflex
If one is very quick with the net, one may see the C-start reflex. In this the fish responds to touch or to sensation of the lateral line on one side, with the contraction of the muscle blocks on the other side. This has the effect of turning the head away from the stimulus and sending the fish shooting off on an alternative course. The fish will swim rapidly for a short while, often at the speed of many bodylengths per second, before coming to rest. Since it is a reflex, the fish has very little control over it and may unwittingly collide with nearby objects. This reflex is inbuilt and is seen

even in larvae - although it is triggered by touch only, the small fry relying on their transparency for initial predator evasion. The key to this reflex are the Mauthner neurons, two large nerves (one either side) which innervate the muscle blocks either side of the backbone. The cell body of these nerves lies on the opposite side to the muscles that they innervate. The Mauthner cells are stimulated by nerve impulses from the lateral line, touch receptors and the acoustic cranial nerve VIII on the same side. Stimulation of any or all of these triggers the Mauthner neurons, which in turn cause muscle contraction on the opposite side of the body, turning the head away from the stimulus. Not only does the Mauthner neuron trigger muscle contraction but it also inhibits the action of its opposite number on the other side. The last trick of the Mauthner neuron is that it also inhibits itself. By causing itself to stop firing, the Mauthner neuron removes the inhibition of the opposite Mauthner neuron, allowing that one to fire and trigger contraction of the other muscle groups. The speed of nerve conduction in these neurons is impressive at 55 metres per second, compared to normal 3 to 10 metres per second.

5.2.4 Metabolic acidosis

Carp can be thought of as having three types of muscle – red, white and pink. The colour varies with the blood supply and the number of mitochondria present. The red muscle has lots of mitochondria and is used for prolonged aerobic exercise such as cruise swimming. The pink muscle has considerably less mitochondria but is well innervated and in carp is also used for cruise swimming, and functions aerobically. White muscle (relatively few mitochondria) is used for short, rapid bursts of activity such as escape responses whilst avoiding capture. The white muscle works anaerobically, that is to say that its contractions do not require oxygen. The downside is that as an end product of anaerobic metabolism by these muscles, large quantities of lactic acid are released into the bloodstream. This causes a fall in blood pH – a metabolic acidosis – that can affect a variety of metabolic functions. Such fish are often badly fatigued and, at best, recovery from this lactic acidosis can take up to twenty-four hours.

This build up of lactic acid may be one of the causes of delayed capture mortality which can cause muscle damage, incoordination, weakness, poor vision and death several days after a stressful capture.

5.2.5 Alarm substance

Koi charging around ponds colliding with other fish, objects and pond walls can lead to damage and loss of scales. Koi have in their epidermis cells called club cells, which produce a substance called pterin. This is also known as alarm substance and is released into the surrounding water when there is damage to the epidermis. Pterin acts as a pheromone and triggers alarm reactions in other fish in the school when picked up by their olfactory organs, so even the fish you do not wish to be captured will become stressed. Also, damaged skin in a stressed and potentially immunosuppressed fish can readily become secondarily infected with bacteria or fungi.

5.2.6 Delayed capture mortality

Delayed capture mortality in fish has been attributed to a variety of causes including blood clotting in the circulation, osmotic disruption, muscle and kidney damage, lactic acidosis and secondary bacterial and viral infections. At least some of these are known to occur in carp.

When catching koi it is best to have assistance and, using two nets, gently persuade the koi into your main net. Allow yourself plenty of time and try to be patient.

5.3.1 Viral infections

5.3.2 Ultra violet radiation

Ultra violet light in the wavelengths of 190 to 300 nm is used extensively with ponds to control suspended algal blooms. A common use is for it to be included in series with the filtration unit such that water is drawn past the bulbs either before or after passing through the filter. UV light has a maximum penetration of around 5-6cm. Much is often made of its virucidal and, indeed, bacteriocidal and protozoal-killing properties but its efficacy depends upon the period of exposure of the pathogen to the UV light. In addition, the UV output falls over a period such that six monthly renewal is recommended.

The output of a UV unit is measured by the number of microwatts delivered in each second for each square centimetre of contact area. The units are uw/sec/cm2. It is suggested that a minimum irradiation for pathogen destruction is 35 000 uw/sec/cm2. However, it can only kill those pathogens that pass by the bulb and, relative to the total volume and surface area available in the pond for pathogen attachment, its use in disease control is likely to be minimal.

5.3.3 Carp Pox

Carp Pox is actually caused by a typical alpha-herpes virus, and is probably better called *Cyprinid Herpes Virus 1* (CHV-1). Affected fish show waxy growths on the body surface and fins, which first make their appearance in late autumn, the number increasing over the winter and into the spring. It is in the spring that it is often first noticed by the koi keeper but, if left untreated, these growths will disappear of their own accord. This is because as the weather improves and temperatures increase, the fish mount an effective immune response, stopping viral production and resolving the wax-like lesions. However, the virus is able to survive in the fish from year to year, lying dormant in the trigeminal nerve and so repeated bouts will occur. Of no great problem to adult fish, it can be devastating in young fry which are not immuno-competent.

CHV-1 can be highly infectious, especially at high stocking densities; external parasites may also be important in spreading the disease.
Treatment : None. Will usually disappear of its own accord, only to return next year.

5.3.4 Spring Viraemia of Carp

Spring Viraemia of Carp (SVC) is caused by a rhabdovirus. Although there have been outbreaks of SVC in the UK, we are considered free of the disease. SVC is notifiable under the Diseases of the Fish Act 1937 (as amended). SVC presents in two main ways:

(a) Usually, the fish will appear bloated due to a build-up of coelomic fluid (ascites); blood spotting is evident and the fish are lethargic and uncoordinated. Gills are often pale and there may be haemorrhage from them. The anus may protrude and trailing faecal casts may be seen.
(b) Alternatively, only the swimbladder is affected, showing marked inflammation and haemorrhages; no other organs are usually involved. Some authorities consider this to be a rhabdovirus distinct from SVC, and it is often referred to as the swim-bladder inflammation (SBI) virus.

Known predisposing factors are low temperatures (viral replication is slowed down, but its ability to cause disease is not affected, so deaths can still occur) and rapidly fluctuating temperatures. At higher temperatures fish are able to mount a better immune response, so fatalities are fewer. Other factors, such as age of the fish and external parasites, are also important in determining the results of an outbreak. SVC is not considered to be in the UK at present.
Treatment: In theory, one would provide supportive treatment such as covering antibiotics. However, in the UK, SVC is notifiable and affected fish stocks may be required to be euthanased.

5.3.5 Gill Necrosis Virus
This suspected iridovirus can be an underlying cause of serious gill pathology. Affected fish will show varying degrees of respiratory distress with mucus trails from the gills. Initially the gills appear thickened and oedematous due to infiltration with white blood cells. The lamellae may stick together. Eventually degeneration occurs with areas of focal necrosis, haemorrhaging and secondary invasion by fungi, bacteria and protozoa. There is no recognised cure. Treat symptomatically as for Bacterial Gill Disease (5.4.8).

5.3.6 Recent reports indicate that in Japan a corona-like virus is associated with skin ulceration and high mortality. Ulceration extends to the muscle layers, and necrotic lesions are also associated with the intestines, spleen, cardiac muscle and the haematopoetic tissue. Extensive damage to this latter may cause an immunosuppression, and indeed secondary bacterial invasion is seen in most, but not all, lesions. Healthy koi infected with cultured virus exhibited the same clinical signs.

5.4.1 Bacterial diseases
The watery medium in which koi live is a potentially hostile environment – the water and the substances either suspended or dissolved in it provide an ideal breeding ground for a vast array of bacteria, some of which will attempt to invade the fish if given an opportunity.
    The koi defence against such an onslaught is its skin which, when intact with an

appropriate mucus layer, provides a fairly impenetrable barrier against bacterial invasion and its immune system.

5.4.2 Predisposing factors

1. Stress. When a koi is unable to adapt completely to its environment, it will be stressed. Obvious stressors include poor water quality, bad handling techniques and inappropriate nutrition. The koi responds to these by releasing "stress hormones" which have the unfortunate side effect of depressing the immune system.

2. Temperature. See 5.1.1. Remember that higher temperatures not only favour the koi immune system but also bacterial multiplication.

3. Endotoxin. Certain bacteria release this, and it can completely suppress the activity of the blood producing tissues throughout the body, as well as the activity of the white blood cells.

4. a) Presence of pathogenic bacteria. The usual bacteria isolated are environmental contaminants such as *Aeromonas species* or *Pseudomonas*. Others occasionally found include *Citrobacter* and *Edwardsiella*. Other important bacterial diseases are the *Mycobacteria* (fish TB) and the Cytophaga-like bacteria (which includes *Flexibacter* and *Cytophaga*).

b) The presence of synergistic bacteria. In most cases of ulcer disease in koi, it is usually *Aeromonas hydrophila* that is isolated. However it is thought that this is a secondary invader, and that it is a different species, *A. salmonicida achromogens*, that is able to form the initial lesion which *A. hydrophila* subsequently invades and swamps out the slower growing *A. salmonicida*.

5. Poor nutrition. Inadequate amounts of food or poor quality food can severely affect the ability of a koi to fend off infection. Stores of the fat-soluble vitamins such as vitamin A can become depleted during the winter months, and extra vitamin C may be useful if the fish is ill. High protein levels help to produce high antibody titres, and essential fatty acids such as polyunsaturated fatty acids (PUFA) have a role in enhancing antibody and macrophage production.

6. Poor water quality. Detectable levels of ammonia and nitrite, high long-term nitrate concentrations, or inappropriate pH and water hardness will eventually create sufficient stress to cause an immunosuppression.

7. Parasites. The fish louse (*Argulus*), Gill flukes (*Dactylogyrus*), skin flukes (*Gyrodactylus*) and the epiphyte (*Epistylis*) *Heteropolaria* have all been associated with initiating bacterial infections. The route of entry of such infections is via the traumatised skin due to the presence of the parasite. Heavy parasite burdens in general will debilitate the fish and make them more susceptible to bacterial infections.

8. Infected individuals. There are three types of such high risk fish – clinically affected fish, asymptommatic carriers and the corpses of dead fish. All three types will contaminate their immediate environment and cadavers eaten by healthy fish provide an easy avenue for infection.

9. Trauma. As a result of bad handling practice, vigorous spawning efforts, heron attacks and so on.

5.4.3 In general, bacterial diseases present as one of three categories: peracute (sudden), acute (fast onset) and chronic (long term).

1) Peracute. This, unfortunately, usually presents as a sudden death with no obvious external signs. Swabs taken during a post-mortem examination will grow large numbers of pathogens. One should rule out water quality problems and poisoning.

2) Acute. Affected fish show classical septicaemic signs, with blood streaking and blotches (haemorrhages) especially on the skin and fins. Other symptoms are behavioural, with the diseased fish losing their appetite, becoming sluggish with fins clamped. Individuals separate from the main group and will be found at the pond edges. Many of these effects are as a result of endotoxins released from the bacteria. Younger fish succumb first, and in a serious outbreak most of those affected may die. It is important to rule out parasitic infections as another possible cause of skin and fin haemorrhages. Another, although still very rare possibility, is Spring Viraemia of Carp (see 5.3.4).

3) Chronic. Ulcerations are probably the commonest presentation of a relatively long-standing bacterial infection. These can vary from being small punctate ulcerations to extensive erosions of the body wall. These ulcers are not only a serious gap in the body's defences but the fish can also suffer from the loss of salts, especially K^+, and the dilution of the body fluids, as it is unable to accurately control its fluid and salt balance. In extreme cases, or if there is marked renal and/or gill damage then ascites will develop, where there is a progressive build up of fluid in the coelomic cavity due to osmosis. Such fish present with a swollen abdomen, exophthalmos and scale protrusion. This latter sign gives the characteristic appearance of "dropsy" caused by the build up of fluid in the scale pockets.
   Presentations can be groups of raised scales where infection has established in the scale pockets causing individual scales to become more prominent. This can progress to true ulceration. The loss of any scales is a potentially serious situation as the scales lie in the dermis (see page 94-95), so by definition their loss involves a breach of the protective epidermal layers. Another presentation that can be seen is long term muscle wastage, especially with the mycobacterial infections. Bacterial Gill Disease is another chronic manifestation involving bacteria,

although the bacteria are only part of the problem and gain a hold on the gills only after poor water quality has damaged these delicate tissues.

5.4.4 Treatment

Treatment should consist of two courses of action. The first is to provide an optimum environment for the fish to recover in. This involves checking on and if necessary correcting any predisposing factors (see 5.4.2). The second is to tackle the disease itself. Where possible raise the water temperature to 20-25°C to stimulate maximum antibody production. Maintaining the koi in a 0.55% sodium chloride solution (built up over three days by adding roughly 1 tablespoon per gallon per day of sea salt or pond salt – not table salt) helps to balance the osmotic difference between the fish and its surrounding medium. This helps to prevent the loss of body salts and the influx of water. The management of ulcers does, to some extent, depend upon their size. Small ulcers may be just left, their healing depending more upon antibiotic medication and enhancing the koi's innate healing capacity. Larger or deep ulcers (Fig 5.2) require some attention, possibly with the need to anaesthetise the fish first. The ulcer is first cleaned up using a proprietary iodine compound such as Tamedine (Vetark). Not only does the iodine kill off most of the bacteria present at the ulcer, but the physical cleaning removes any dead or devitalised tissues that inhibit normal healing. It may be beneficial to coat the cleaned ulcer with Orabase (Convatec). Orabase is a paste designed to be applied to mucous membranes, especially mouth ulcers in man. It will act as an osmotic barrier and may also prevent the entry of opportunist fungi. Expect the Orabase to swell up and drop off within a short while, but hopefully a thin layer will remain to act as a barrier. As the ulcer heals, skin cells migrate in from the circumference of the ulcer (and underneath the layer of Orabase if used) to cover the breach in the skin and providing some waterproofing (Fig 5.3). As these cells are recruited from the surrounding skin, the epidermis around the ulcer becomes thinner.

   This healing event is largely independent of ambient temperature. Once this re-epithelialisation is complete the ulcer then fills up by division of these epidermal cells, a process the rate of which is dictated by the surrounding temperature (Fig 5.4). Repetitive cleaning of ulcers is therefore not recommended as this can actually slow down the healing process due to continual removal of the inwardly migrating skin cells. Eventually healing is complete – the site of the lesion may stand proud of the surrounding skin for a while (Fig 5.5), but it will eventually remodel. Scales may regenerate if the scale pocket is not too badly damaged. Culture and antibiotic sensitivity testing is very important to help choose the right antibiotic.

5.4.5 Prevention

The risk of bacterial disease can be minimised by the following:

1. **Good husbandry practices.** Pay particular attention to water quality and watch out for any problems that could be placed upon the list of predisposing factors.

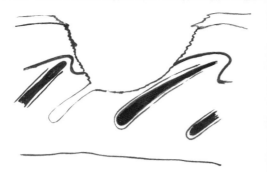

◄ Fig 5.1 A section through an ulcer, showing loss of one scale.

► Fig 5.2 There is invasion of epithelial cells and mucus from the surrounding epidermis.

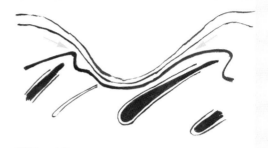

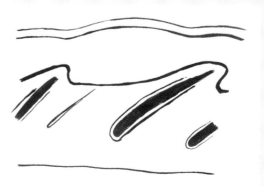

◄ Fig 5.3 Division of epithelial cells allows a progressive infilling of the ulcer.

► Fig 5.4 The epidermis is now full thickness, restoring the protective and osmotic barrier between the koi and surrounding water.

2. **Infeed immunostimulants.** These work in two ways. The glucomannans (or glucans) work by stimulating macrophages so that they consume more bacteria, as well as inducing an increase in bacteria destroying enzymes. Others called manna oligosaccharides actually bind to the lining of the gut thereby preventing pathogenic bacteria from gaining a foothold.

3. **Vaccination.** There are vaccines available specifically against *A.salmonicida* which, as outlined above, appears to be the initial culprit in the majority of *Aeromonas* outbreaks.

4. **Euthanasia.** This can be applied to two groups of fish – those that are chronically ill with little or no chance of cure, such as those with fish TB, and those which are identified as asymptommatic carriers of infection.

5.4.6 *Aeromonas* (carp erythrodermatitis)/*Pseudomonas* infections

Aeromonas salmonicida achromogens is a pathogen in its own right, whereas *Aeromonas hydrophila* and *Pseudomonas* species are secondary, opportunist invaders. *Aeromonas* and *Pseudomonas* bacteria are common inhabitants of freshwater habitats, and are also present naturally, both on fish, and as part of their flora.

Low temperatures, or rapidly oscillating temperatures, have been associated with an increase in bacterial numbers on the gills, skin and in the intestines of carp. As the temperature in spring continues to warm up, the immune system becomes more proficient. Unfortunately, bacterial replication also increases, as does their ability to cause disease.

Treatment: Antibiotics by injection, in food or in a special treatment. Which antibiotic will depend upon laboratory sensitivity tests. Large ulcers may require cleaning and topical treatment, often with the fish anaesthetised.

5.4.7 Cytophaga-like bacteria

Peduncle disease/coldwater disease is a slowly progressive disease caused primarily by *Cytophaga psychrophila*. This disease is considered a secondary infection, occurring when the fish are otherwise stressed. Ideal temperatures for growth are in the range of -1 to 10°C - precisely the range in which the Koi immune system is least able to handle the infection. The disease often starts as a fin rot, but then progresses down to the base of the fin to form a large ulcer, which may become deep enough to expose the vertebrae.

Treatment: As for Aeromonas/Pseudomonas.

5.4.8 Bacterial Gill Disease

This is a complex disorder, probably resulting from a combination of adverse environmental condition and the presence of bacteria of varying disease-causing ability.

BGD manifests itself by the fish becoming lethargic and off their food, plus an increased respiratory rate, coughing, flared gill covers and mucus strings trailing from the gills. Outbreaks in carp have been known to occur at temperatures as low as 5°C. *Treatment: As for Aeromonas/Pseudomonas. A salt water bath (10- 20g/L) for 1-2 minutes will help, as will chloramine-T for one hour. The dose of chloramine-T is dependant upon water hardness and pH.*

5.4.9 Lactobacillus piscicola
This is regarded as a normal commensal and may cause problems following spawning or rough handling. Often presents as a septicaemic condition with internal haemorrhages, ascites (dropsy) and kidney granulomas.
Treatment: As for Aeromonas/Pseudomonas.

5.4.10 *Edwardsiella* Septicaemia
E. tarda has been known to cause septicaemia in koi. Infections are probably associated with poor water quality, high water temperatures and overcrowding.
Treatment: As for Aeromonas/Pseudomonas.

5.4.11 Columnaris Disease
Outbreaks due to *Flexibacter columnaris* usually occur at temperatures over 15°C (59°F) in conditions stressful to koi. External tissues are attacked first of all, with the fins and gills being prime targets. Erosions appear, often with a reddened rim. Eventually, the bacteria invade the bloodstream and there is a terminal spread to the internal organs. If one takes a skin scraping, under light microscopy at medium power, *F. columnaris* can often be visualised as "haystacks" at edge of the mucus sample. Useful as *Flexibacter* is difficult to culture.
Treatment: Columnaris may respond to a benzalkonium chloride bath. The toxicity of benzalkonium chloride is increased in soft water and doses should be reduced in soft water, or if softness not known.

Chloramine-T Dose (mg/l)

pH	Soft water	Hard water
6.0	2.5	7.0
6.5	5.0	10.0
7.0	10.0	15.0
7.5	18.0	18.0
8.0	20.0	20.0

Benzalkonium Chloride

Dose (mg/l)	Duration of Bath
10	5 – 10 minutes
5	30 minutes
2	60 minutes
1	Several hours

5.4.12 Botulism

In deep earthen ponds with a heavy sediment layer, anaerobic conditions can develop which, at temperatures over 12 to 15°C, can favour the growth of *Clostridium botulinum*. Intoxication may occur following ingestion of the sediment or disturbance of it. Affected fish are initially uncoordinated, but eventually become paralysed and die.
Treatment: No known cure.

5.4.13 Fish tuberculosis

Classically, this disease is caused by infections with either *Mycobacterium marinum* or *M. fortuitum* (although other species may be involved). This is a long term, debilitative disease which can present in a variety of ways, depending upon which organ(s) is/are affected. Common presentations include long-term weight loss or spinal curvature (due to collapse of infected vertebrae). Potential zoonosis, classically causing granulomas on extremities such as fingers.
Treatment: Problematic. This disease is infectious to man. Consider humane destruction of fish if diagnosed.

5.5.1 Chylamidia-like organisms

5.5.2 Epitheliocystis is caused by intracellular, bacteria-like pathogens which have yet to be definitively classified. They seem to infect the mucus-secreting cells in the gills and skin of carp, where transparent or whitish cysts are formed. In large numbers they cause damage to the gills, and respiratory distress partially due to excessive mucus production. In carp, especially, there is a proliferative reaction, which can be associated with low temperatures, in which the surrounding tissues form a significant fleshy mass. In appearance, Epitheliocystis can be difficult to distinguish from the iridioviral infection *Lymphocystis*. However, *Lymphocystis* does not infect carp.
Treatment: Limited information available. May respond to chloramphenicol at 40mg/kg i.m daily. Long term use may be immunosuppressive.

5.6.1 Fungal Disease

5.6.2 *Saprolegnia*

Needs no introduction: this is the classic freshwater disease which afflicts most freshwater fish. Typically, this presents as a cottonwool-like growth, and can affect any part of the fish.

Fungal spores are present in the environment and infections are usually secondary to other infections, trauma or stress. Low temperatures favour growth of the fungus because of the associated immune suppression.
Treatment: Gently remove as much of the fungus as possible and swab with a 10% solution of povidone-iodine. Malachite Green Bath at 2mg/l for 30 minutes. Once is often sufficient but watch out for respiratory distress (see 7.1.8).

5.6.3 *Branchiomycosis*

Branchiomycosis sanguinis infections are usually referred to as Gill Rot, because this fungus invades the gill tissue. Affected fish gasp at the surface, and appear weak and lethargic. Examination will often reveal raised, plaque-like areas of abnormal gill tissue. Although the disease is often fatal, some fish will recover, regenerating their damaged gill tissue. Gill Rot is often associated with poor water quality, overcrowding, algal blooms and temperatures over 20°C.
Treatment: No known effective treatment. Concentrate on maintenance of optimum water quality and stocking densities.

5.6.4 *Dermocystidium koi*

This possesses characteristics of both fungi and protozoa, although it is usually regarded as a fungus. It causes cysts in the muscles and skin and, occasionally, gills. As the fungus grows, extra hyphae are produced and are visible through the thinned surface of the lesion as a mass of fine, cotton-like material. The life cycle is unknown, but eventually the cysts rupture releasing thousands of spores into the environment. *There is no recognised treatment, although self-healing may occur following rupture. Consider surgical removal if appropriate.* Dermocystidium *rarely causes problems.*

5.7.1 Protozoal Parasites

5.7.2 *Hoferellus cyprini*

H. cyprini is a kidney parasite of carp which become infected after eating infested tubificid worms. Badly infected fish are off-colour, stop feeding and progressively lose their balance until they die after around 7 to 14 days. Spring is the time when carrier fish shed spores into the pond water in their urine.
Treatment: No known treatment. Attempt to restrict access of koi to tubificid worms (impossible?).

5.7.3 Trypanoplasma species

Trypanoplasms are parasites found in the blood. Those of potential importance to koi are *T. cyprini, T. borreli* and *T. tincae.*

Fortunately for the UK koi population, this infection needs to be transmitted by leeches, including *Piscicola geometra*, and so only those stocks living in or brought in from natural waters will be at real risk. Affected fish are anorexic, listless, show weight loss and are anaemic. Blood clotting is reduced.

Times of greatest risk are over winter - when the koi immune system is depressed - and late spring when there are large numbers of leeches around.
Treatment: Methylene blue by mouth at 60mg.kg/day for four days, or metronidazole at 50mg/kg/day. Best controlled by elimination of leeches.

5.7.4 *Ichtyobodo necator*

Formerly called *Costia necatrix,* this ectoparasite is able to survive temperatures down to 2°C. Even at this low temperature, massive infestations have been described in hibernating carp.

The first obvious signs are dull areas on the skin due to secondary mucus production in response to the parasite. Badly affected fish lose their appetite, swim with their fins clamped and may scrape against objects. The skin becomes reddened, then haemorrhagic, while the gills are pale and covered in thick mucus. *Saprolegnia* is a common secondary invader.

Treatment: Use a proprietary ectoparasitic treatment or glacial acetic acid dips at 8ml per gallon, for 30-45 seconds.

5.7.5 *Chilodonella cyprini*

These motile protozoa graze on epithelial (lining) cells of the gills and skin. The irritation caused results in excessive mucus production, as well as clamped fins, respiratory distress and depression.

Temperatures of 5-10°C (41-50°F) seem to be close to the optimum for *C. cyprini*, giving them a significant headstart on the koi immune system in spring.

Treatment: Use a proprietary ectoparasitic treatment. Also formaldehyde at 25ppm, followed by a water change in 4 to 8 hours, or salt at 3g/l until symptoms stop.

5.7.6 *Ichthyophthirius*

The White Spot Disease parasite has a complicated life cycle, with stages both on the fish and in the environment. The environmental temperature modulates the life cycle of *Icthyophthirius multifiliis*. At 24-26°C it is completed in around four days, whereas at 5°C it takes 35-40 days. During the winter months, the replication of the parasite is therefore slowed but not arrested, giving it a numerical advantage as temperatures rise in the spring. However, koi are able to mount a good immune response, especially at temperatures greater than 12°C, so that healthy fish will eventually shake off the infestation.

Koi stressed by severe overwintering conditions or other factors may not be so fortunate, with the associated immune suppression allowing large numbers of *Ichthyophthirius* cysts (which are the white spots) to establish – look for a white pepper-dusting effect. These cysts can cause severe damage to the gills and skin, and also allow secondary infections to establish. Infections can build up rapidly, and mortalities can occur, especially if the gills are heavily parasitised.

Treatment: Use a proprietary White Spot Remedy.

5.7.7 *Epistylis*

Also known as *Heteropolaria*, the *Epistylis* protozoan is basically a commensal, that is to say that it uses the fish purely as a surface on which to attach itself. Given conditions stressful to the host fish, such as lowered winter and spring temperatures, and high levels of organic matter in the water, *Epystilis* can increase in numbers, forming whitish fuzzy patches which may progress to form ulcers in the skin. Secondary infection then occurs, with fish losses resulting from classic bacterial

septicaemia. An attempt should be made to distinguish *Epistylis* from *Saprolegnia*, as the two conditions can appear similar; this is best achieved with a basic light microscope.
Treatment: Salt at 22g/l for 30 minutes every 7 days for 3 weeks.

5.7.8 *Trichodiniasis*
Actually, there are three genera falling under this title - *Trichodina*, *Trichodonella* and *Triparciella*. Infested fish produce excessive mucus and so have a greyish cast; later, skin erosions can form. The gills are also badly affected. In fact, in Koi, infestations may be limited to the gills alone. Affected fish will scratch and may show laboured breathing or inflamed gills.
Treatment: Products containing formalin should be effective, or give salt bath at 10-15g/litre for twenty minutes.

5.7.9 Oodinium (Velvet) Disease
O. pillularis can cause explosive outbreaks of disease, affected fish showing the characteristic greyish velvet-like film on the body surface.

Infected fish are itchy, constantly scratching and may stop feeding. The gills may also be affected. *O. pillularis* contains chlorophyll and, under ideal lighting and temperatures (23 to 25°C), can become infective within 2-3 days.
Treatment: Use a proprietary ectoparasitic treatment containing either formalin or copper.

5.7.10 *Trypanosoma danilewskyi*
This is a haemoparasite that is transmitted by the fish leech, *Piscicola geometra*. These parasites are really only a threat to debilitated fish. Affected fish are lethargic, with pale gills due to anaemia.
Treatment: Try as for Trypanoplasma species – methylene blue by mouth at 60mg.kg/day for four days, or metronidazole at 50mg/kg/day. Best controlled by elimination of leeches.

5.7.11 Sporozoon parasites
This group of parasites contains a number of species pathogenic to koi. Included are *Shaerospora renicola* (see 4.2.3), *Chloromyxum cyrini* and *C. koi* (which infect the gallbladder), *Myxosoma dujardini* and *M. encephalina*. The first of these Myxosomas causes yellow-white cysts in the gills, leading to breathing difficulties and death; the second infects the blood vessels of the brain.

Henneguya koi manifests as small, smooth rounded "cysts" or nodules in a variety of organs, especially the gills and skin. This is an intracellular parasite which forms large pseudocysts (the nodules) from which large numbers of spores are eventually released. This happens at the death of the fish, although skin nodules may rupture. It is best to remove affected individuals as they may pose a risk of infection.

Eimeria carpelli and *E. subepithelialis* both cause significant disease in young carp, those weighing less than 25g being especially susceptible. Typically in early spring before the carp start to feed losses are seen, with those surviving showing marked weight loss. A more severe disease, *E. carpelli,* causes severe enteritis with reddened, hyperaemic gut mucosa. The parasite is found in the lamina mucosa. *E. subepithelialis* presents as small, whitish nodules from 1-3mm diameter in the lamina submucosa. *Treatment: No effective treatment. Fumigillin at 1g/kg food for 10-14 days has been used for prevention of Shaerospora renicola. Eimerias may respond to anticoccidial drugs such as amprolium as a continuous bath at 10mg/l for 7-10 days or to sulphonamide antibiotics (see 4.2.6).*

5.8.1 Helminths

5.8.2 Skin Flukes
Skin Flukes (*Gyrodactylus*) are live bearers and are characterised by large, paired hooks which they use to anchor themselves to the skin. This live-bearing means of reproduction allows for rapid, temperature-related multiplication. They can be a serious cause of skin irritation, typified by areas of increased mucus production. Occasionally, the gills are affected.

5.8.3 Gill Flukes
Gill Flukes (*Dactylogyrus*) can cause serious damage to the gills, as they can be very destructive. Dactylogyrids are egglayers, with their life cycle shortened to a few days at 22-24°C. *Dactylogyrus* are significant pathogens, worsened by the fact that their eggs are resistant to treatment, hence repeat medications are required.
Treatment for Skin and Gill Flukes : Praziquantel as a 3 hour bath at 10mg/litre or 400mg/100g food daily for 7 days. It is advisable to repeat treatment after 3 weeks for the egg-laying Dactylogyrids.

5.8.4 Tapeworms
The tapeworms *Bothriocephalus* and *Khawia* are found as adults in carp, with intermediate stages occurring in copepods (*Bothriocephalus*) and in tubificid worms (*Khawia*). Peak infection time for *Bothriocephalus* is mid-summer. *Khawia* has a peak in late spring, falling in midsummer, then increasing from mid-July onwards. Though unlikely to be a problem in adult Koi, both parasites can be devastating in young fish. Young koi parasitised with *Bothriocephalus* become inappetant, emaciated and swim at the surface. The coelomic cavity can become enlarged and the walls of the intestine so thin that the tapeworms can be seen through them on post-mortem examination. *Treatment: Praziquantel as above. Probably not feasible to control intermediate hosts.*

5.8.5 *Sanguinicola inermis*
These are digenetic trematodes (flukes) which live as adults in the major blood vessels and occasionally the heart of carp. Eating the intermediate hosts – aquatic snails - infects the fish. The schistosome-like eggs lodge in the gill vessels where they hatch, damaging the gills and causing haemorrhage and extensive damage. The life-cycle takes around six weeks at temperatures greater than 20°C. Some eggs find

their way to other organs such as the kidneys where they die and become encysted providing historical histological evidence of infection. Check filtration systems for presence of snails
Treatment: Oral praziquantel may be effective: (see above). Use of molluscicides to control snail population.

5.8.6 *Diplostomum sphathaceum*
This is a trematode that has a three host life-cycle. Intermediate life-cycle stages (cercariae) are released from aquatic snails as temperatures rise. The cercariae find and penetrate carp – small fry can be killed but older ones survive. The metacercariae migrate to the eyes and invade the lens causing a blindness that makes them susceptible to the primary host – piscivorous aquatic birds.
Treatment: Praziquantel (see 5.8.2) may be effective or consider enucleation if very bad. Control of other hosts with molluscicides to reduce the snail population and improve pond defences against fish-eating birds.

5.8.7 Leeches
The main species are *Piscicola geometra* and *Hemiclepsis marginata*. Unlikely in a prepared pond, but common in natural ponds. One leech is unlikely to cause a problem although they can remain attached for up to four weeks. However very small fish can be killed. Can be a vector for SVC, *Aeromonas* infections and haemoparasites (*Trypanoplasma* [5.7.3] and *Trypanosomes* [5.7.10]).
Treatment: Glacial Acetic acid dips for individual cases at 8ml per gallon, for 30-45 seconds. Control of indigenous populations could be attempted with dichlorvos as for crustaceans but the ramifications of using such a product in a natural pond must be considered seriously.

5.9.1 Crustacea

5.9.2 *Argulus* (Fish louse)
Visible to the naked eye, this flattened crustacean parasite not only causes irritation to its host but may also introduce secondary infections on its mouthparts. Egg production starts at 16°C and, at ideal temperatures, the life cycle takes around 40 days. The eggs are laid in strips in the environment and this stage is very resistant so repeat treatments may be necessary.

5.9.3 *Lernaea* (Anchor Worm)
The head of this crustacean lie buried in the skin or gill tissue of the host, creating some irritation and a site for secondary infection. Mature females possess two egg sacs near the posterior of the body, producing a Y-shape. The life-cycle cannot be completed below 15°C.

5.9.4 *Ergasilus* (Gill Maggots)
These copepod crustaceans are found usually attached to the gills where the females

with egg sacs are readily apparent. Gill damage can be severe and may provide a source for secondary infection.

Treatment for Crustacea: Fish Lice (Argulus),and Anchor Worm (Lernaea) and Gill Maggots (Ergasilus) Can be problematic: remove individual Argulus and Lernaea, manually, and treat ponds with dichlorvos (an organophosphate licensed for use in salmon). Consult manufacturers for suggested dose regimes.

5.10.1 Molluscs

In late spring, Koi kept in waters containing freshwater mussels may find themselves temporary hosts to glocchidia, the parasitic immature stage of these mussels. Generally little lasting harm is done although the glocchidia may prove an irritation. There is a slight risk of secondary infection at the sites of attachment once the glocchidia leave their host.

Treatment: Will detach of their own accord. Damaged skin may require attention as outlined above for ulcers.

8.2.1 Zoonoses

These are diseases transmissible to man. Unlike with mammalian pets, fortunately there are very few of these that are associated with koi.

8.2.2 Mycobacteriosis (see also 5.4.13)

Mycobacteria often infect the bowel and kidneys of fish, allowing the excretion of the organism into the general environment. This is usually where the unfortunate fishkeeper risks infection as the mycobacteria are able to invade cuts and abrasions in the skin to establish localised infections. The hands are the usual site of these infections, as they are the parts most likely to be exposed.

Strains isolated from fish grow best at 18-20°C. In man, this usually limits the infection to the skin surface at the extremities such as the fingers, where temperature is relatively low. Occasionally there is some temperature adaptation into the region of 30-33°C, which may allow some further spread. Usually this involves the lymphatics giving rise to multiple, painful, raised and reddened lesions. More serious infections are rare.

Treatment involves a combination of excision plus appropriate antibiosis.

8.2.3 Nocardia

This is an occasional cause of "tuberculosis" in fish, although its source is likely to be surrounding soil rather than it acting as a true fish disease. It has been associated with pericarditis in man.

8.2.4 Salmonella

Occasionally linked with fish, there is no evidence for it as a fish pathogen or, indeed, as a normal fish commensal. If it is found associated with fish then it is more likely to be transient, introduced infeed or from environmental contamination. Serotypes isolated to date have not been those usually associated with human disease.

8.2.5 Other bacteria, namely *Aeromonas, Edwardsiella* and *Pseudomonas,* are all recognised as occasional pathogens in man, although their occurrence is usually associated with vulnerable groups such as the very young, elderly or those on immunosuppressive medication.

8.2.6 Leptospirosis

Also known as Wiel's Disease, this is due to infection with the spirochaete bacterium *Leptospira icterohaemorragica*. It is a true zoonosis but the source of infection is not koi but wild rats in and around ponds.

It presents a serious risk to man because:

1. The natural source is a mammal and so it is adapted to live at 37°C in mammalian tissue.

2. *Leptospira icterohaemorragica* can survive for some time (up to several weeks) as long as their environment is damp. Drying rapidly kills these bacteria.

3. Cuts and abrasions on wet hands provide easy portals of entry for leptospirae – in fact they are able to penetrate intact skin providing it is wet.

Symptoms in man vary from mild, flu-like fever and aching to a severe renal inflammation and jaundice. Death may occur if untreated.

8.2.7 Reducing zoonotic risks

1. Pay strict attention to personal hygiene following contact with ponds, aquaria or handling fish. Avoid wiping wet hands across mouth and eyes. If there is a risk of Wiel's Disease, wash one's hands with vinegar as the low pH will kill the leptospirae.

2. Cover cuts and scrapes with waterproof band aids or gloves.

3. Avoid using your mouth to start a syphon during routine water changes.

4. Pay attention to husbandry. This will prevent the build up of excessive levels of bacteria. Correct diet and husbandry will reduce stress, helping to promote natural resistance.

5. Biological filtration may reduce the presence of zoonotic bacteria in ponds and aquaria by establishing an unsuitable environment in the substrate/filters, possibly by providing competitive bacteria for nutrients and living space. *Leptospira icterohaemorragica* survives longer in stagnant water than flowing water.

6. Pond owners should take care to store fish food in rodent-proof containers to discourage rats. Site bird tables away from ponds. If you suspect rats, consult a professional pest controller.

7. Tackle any outbreaks of disease promptly. In the case of mycobacteriosis, euthanasia of affected fish may be required as treatment is often unrewarding.

8. If you have any worries at all, consult your GP.

Chapter Six
Non-infective Factors and Disorders

6.1.1 Environmental Disorders

6.1.2 Temperature
First of all the ambient temperature affects not only the koi but also the filter bacteria. Hence, monitoring of water quality is vitally important – check levels of ammonia and nitrite particularly to make sure that the biological filtration is keeping pace with your koi.

6.1.3 pH
Check the pH as, although your concrete pond may be sealed, the concrete and cement used around the pond edge may not be, and the rain run-off from these areas into the pond may be causing the pH to rise.

6.1.4 Lightning
The uncertain spring weather can also bring problems of another kind – lightning strike has been put forward as an explanation for a sudden outbreak of broken backs in koi in a pool, the supercharge of electricity in the vicinity of the pool causing powerful contractions of the muscles along the spinal column, sufficiently strong to fracture some vertebrae.

Other causes of spinal deformities would include mycobacterial infections (5.4.13), neoplasia, heavy metal toxicity (1.12.1), pesticides (6.1.8) and vitamin C deficiency (6.2.5).

6.1.5 Algal blooms
These can become problematic in the spring and summer, and not just from an aesthetic point of view. Certain suspended algae, such as *Chlorella*, secrete toxins that can interfere with breeding. A massive die-off of such algal blooms can produce a lot of decaying material in the pond, producing serious oxygen depletion. Heavily planted ponds can also suffer from a lack of oxygen during the night, when the plants are no longer able to photosynthesise (which produces oxygen) but continue to respire (which uses oxygen).

Carp are able to survive in water with poor oxygen levels by a combination of gulping in atmospheric air at the surface and using certain anaerobic (non-oxygen requiring) metabolic pathways, but it is still very stressful for them. During the night, not only are the plants using up oxygen, but they are also releasing carbon dioxide as a by-product of respiration (as do fish). This carbon dioxide is very water-soluble, forming carbonic acid. Therefore during the day, as the plants photosynthesise, carbon dioxide and even bicarbonate ions are removed from the water which, in turn, causes an increase in pH, reaching a peak shortly before sundown.

Ponds with an overwhelming plant growth can therefore experience major pH swings over a 24-hour period, the pH rapidly falling at night only to rise once more the following morning as the dissolved carbon dioxide is removed from solution by the plants photosynthesising again. Ponds experiencing extreme algal blooms may be subject to super-saturation of the water with oxygen during the daylight hours. Fish in such ponds will often show signs of :-

6.1.6 Gas Bubble Disease

Bubbles of oxygen forming in the blood vessels of the skin, fins and behind the eyes.
Treatment: All the problems associated with algal blooms can be avoided by installing ultra-violet units and increasing the pool aeration. Increased aeration will even help to prevent oxygen super-saturation, associated with Gas Bubble Disease. See 1.9.6 (ii).

6.1.7 Sunburn

Koi swimming close to the surface, in clear water with no cover, may suffer from sunburn. This should be suspected if there is a lesion on the dorsal aspect (back) only, possibly including the dorsal fin. White areas, lacking the protection of pigmentation, may be particularly affected.
Treatment: Treat any lesions as for ulceration. Provide access to suitable cover.

6.1.8 Herbicides and pesticides

All these compounds should be regarded as poisonous to fish and have no place in or around a water garden. For example, a random gust of wind may blow a mist of the chemical over your pool surface; or rainwater may wash it into the pond; or dead or dying insects may drop on to the water surface, where they are greedily consumed by koi.
Treatment: Avoid using these compounds around ponds. Due to the wide range of chemicals used, each with different effects, diagnosis is difficult and treatment rarely possible.

6.1.9 Medications

Formalin, a common ingredient of proprietary ectoparasitic preparations, lowers the levels of oxygen in the water, as well as being toxic to gill tissue. Combine this with warm water, with its reduced oxygen-holding capacity, and there could be trouble.

Malachite Green is more toxic at temperatures greater than 21°C, injuring the gills and blocking digestive enzymes. Malachite green blocks respiratory enzymes at mitochondrial level and so extra oxygenation will have little effect.
Treatment: Always make sure that the water is well aerated, especially where products containing formalin are concerned.

6.1.10 Trauma

Fish can be traumatised during capture or predatory attack. Classic predators would include herons but in the USA raccoons can be a problem. Frogs and toads during the breeding season may invade koi ponds where the males reflexly grasp passing koi in a mimicked amplexus, causing damage or even death if the operculae are clamped shut by this embrace.

Spawning is not, of course, a disease nor a disorder but a very frantic, physical and potentially traumatic event. It leaves the fish exhausted, stressed and often damaged and susceptible to secondary infections.

Treatment: Clean up and treat as appropriate. Remember that the scales are embedded in the skin, so scale loss will produce a serious skin defect.

6.2.1 Metabolic Disorders

6.2.2 Dystocia (Egg-binding)

A bad spring can lead to problems further on in the year. A classic example of this is dystocia. Development of the ovaries and the eggs inside them is temperature-dependant prior to ovulation and spawning. In other words, there needs to be a certain number of days at a sufficiently high temperature for correct ovarian maturation. In addition the eggs do not lie free in the coelomic cavity (as in trout) and considerable effort is required to expel the eggs. This is provided by a vigorous spawning chase, often involving several males, where the powerful contractions of the body wall musculature helps to squeeze out the eggs.

If there is a poor spring, then the ovaries may not develop sufficiently to allow normal spawning to take place, giving a build-up of immature eggs. This problem is worsened by the fact that egg development is not synchronised, so that eggs are continuously produced (given ideal conditions, koi will spawn several times during the breeding season). These eggs can eventually be reabsorbed but it can take up to two years if conditions are not favourable. In many collections there may not be sufficient or large enough males to chase bigger females and so they are unable to shed their ripe eggs.

Dystocia in koi is probably not fatal in itself but it is an extra stress upon these fish, making them more susceptible to other disorders.

Treatment: Tricky. Prime the fish with carp pituitary injections. Supplied as a freeze dried preparation that needs to be reconstituted with sterile saline or water, the dose rate is initially 0.3mg/kg as a lower, priming dose, with a second given 12-18 hours later at 3.0mg/kg. Manual spawning should be attempted 6-12 hours afterwards. Raise environmental temperature to around 25°C.

6.2.3 Hepatic Lipidosis (Fatty Liver Disease)

In the wild, carp spend a large part of the day foraging for food. This is partially because they lack a stomach, and so are unable to store one large meal to digest at leisure, and partially because much of their natural diet is nutritionally poor so significant quantities need to be ingested. In captivity, koi are usually fed high quality, energy-rich diets. Any excess foods not used to provide energy for swimming, egg production, metabolism and the like will be converted to fats and stored, particularly in the liver. Over time, these stores can become so great that normal liver function is disrupted. In addition, relatively low levels of dietary vitamin E will fail to prevent this fat oxidising (turning rancid) over time, with a damaging release of free radicals and ketone production. Unfortunately, hepatic lipidosis is usually diagnosed at post mortem. Force feeding energy-rich diets to accelerate the growth of young koi can bring about a similar situation.

Treatment: Avoid excessive feeding and supplement with extra dietary vitamin E. Feed lower protein and fat diet to remaining fish.

6.2.4 Sekoke Disease
Advanced cases of vitamin E deficiency result in Sekoke Disease (appetite loss, poor growth, muscle wastage and death), which will not be seen if one feeds a good-quality brand of food.

Treatment: Supplement with extra vitamin E.

6.2.5 Vitamin C
Early work with farmed carp found that there appeared to be no requirement for dietary vitamin C. However it appears that in koi there *is* a definite vitamin C need and it seems to be necessary for normal immune function (5.4.2[5]). In addition spinal deformities are often said to be associated with a hypovitaminosis C, possibly due to effects upon collagen and cartilage integrity and formation. Most commercial koi foods have enhanced (stabilised) vitamin C levels, although these will fall over time or if kept in poor storage conditions.

6.2.6 Pigmentation
These impart colour to the skin, flesh and eggs of fish and include the carotenoids, xanthophylls and pterins. The most important for ornamental carp are leutin, zeaxanthin, and taraxanthin (yellow pigments) and astazanthin and canthaxanthin (red pigments). Certain algae such as *Chlorella vulgaris* and *Scenedesmus quadricaudatus* are occasionally incorporated into commercial diets because of their high carotinoid content. The efficiency of pigmentors varies with the levels of dietary fats, its oxidative state and the presence or absence of antioxidants.

Koi metabolise zeaxanthin (yellow) to astaxanthin (red) although very little beta-carotene and no leutin are converted to astaxanthin. Canthaxanthin may be important in the onset of spawning and fertilisation.

6.3.1 Neoplasia
Koi are potentially very long-lived (up to 60 years) and, as in all animals, tumours can be found in older specimens. In addition, long-term exposure to water pollutants can induce tumour formation. Some of the tumours recorded in koi are adenocarcinomas of pancreatic origin and intestine, hepatocellular tumours, fibromas and thyroid adenoma.

Treatment: Surgical removal may be possible if tumour small. Euthanase fish if tumour interferes with normal function or behaviour.

6.3.2 Erythrophoroma
Known as *hukkui* to hobbyists, this presents as a swelling of red pigmented tissue in the skin which causes little scale disruption. Rarely causes problems although a superficial keratectomy may be necessary in the rare cases of corneal involvement.

6.3.3 Papillomatosis
The appearance can vary from areas of epidermal hyperplasia to genuine cauliform masses. Usually considered benign, in some cases these can progress to squamous cell carcinomas. A viral aetiology has been suggested, as has water pollutants.

6.4.1 Ophthalmic Disorders

6.4.2 Exophthalmos
Often seen accompanying ascites (see 2.1.2), it can be due to a variety of conditions including trauma, bacterial disease, neoplasia, ammonium toxicity (see 1.6.5), gas bubble disease (1.9.6) and ocular parasites (5.8.7). If the condition is unilateral strongly consider the possibility of a retrobulbar space-occupying lesion such as a neoplasm or a mycobacterial granuloma.

6.4.3 Keratitis
Usually secondary to trauma. The eye will have a superficially cloudy appearance due to localised excess mucus production (a protective mechanism). In extreme cases there may be traumatic ulceration of the cornea. Such eyes are probably functionally lost, so enucleation should be considered as a means of removing a possible source of infection.

6.4.4 Papillomas
Often appear as raised nodules on the cornea (as well as elsewhere on the body, see 6.3.3).

6.4.5 Cataracts
A cataract is opacity of the lens. Although reported in other species as being due to nutritional deficiencies, parasitism and excessive exposure to ultra violet light, in koi it appears to be rare. It may occasionally be seen in older koi as an ageing change.

6.5.1 Hypersensitivity Reactions
May present as sterile ulcerative lesions. Diagnosed on histopathological examination to demonstrate cellular skin changes consistent with a hypersensitivity, or allergic reaction. Possible triggers could be external parasites such as *Argulus* (5.9.2) and *Learnea* (5.9.3).

Chapter Seven
Seasonal Husbandry

7.1.1 Winter wind-down
As Autumn procedes with shortening days and lower average temperatures, koi begin to undergo a series of physiological changes that will help them to survive through the winter. These changes involve alterations to the muscle, nervous system, blood and metabolic pathways. Genes in the liver are triggered which increase the production of non-esterified fats incorporated into myelin sheaths and other cell membranes, because they are less likely to solidify at lower temperatures. Another important consequence of lowered temperatures is the suppression of the fishes' immune system, such that fish are less able to deal with infections (although, fortunately, the disease processes of most infections are slowed down).

7.1.2 Vegetation
Vegetation in the water comes from both in and around the pond. Dealing with aquatic vegetation first, autumn is the time to cut back water lilies and other plants as the leaves start to die. Leaves from surrounding deciduous trees can be a problem and are best dealt with by covering the pond with a net, or using a skimmer.

In both cases, if vegetation is left to decompose then water quality, as is often repeated, can suffer badly, stressing koi and putting them at a disadvantage.

7.1.3 Filters
Filters can be cleaned out at this time of year, as there is plenty of time for the beneficial bacteria to recolonise the media before winter temperatures slow down the bacterial proliferation. With multi-chambered filters, clean out one chamber per week. If you have the facility, change the pond intake from the bottom drains to one part way up the water column. This tends to preserve a static, deeper layer of water which, thanks to the unusual properties of water, will remain at around 4°C irrespective of the weather above the surface, providing an ideal place to sit out the coldest months.

Ponds which do not have this facility, or which are not deep enough, will subject the koi to a constant water flow, forcing them to swim, thus using up valuable energy reserves and exposing them to water being continuously cooled by its journey through the filtration unit. Reducing the water flow will help, but this should not be stopped altogether, as the bacterial colonies, necessary for the filter's function, will be starved of oxygen.

7.1.4 Examinations
If possible it is worthwhile gently catching each and every fish in early autumn, giving them a quick examination to check for small ulcers, external parasites and the like. Any obvious lesions or infections should be dealt with at this time, if necessary isolating individuals in a heated treatment vat to encourage rapid healing before the fish are exposed to the rigours of winter.

7.1.5 Feeding
As the average water temperature starts to drop, our thoughts turn towards the vexing subject of feeding. Koi see out the coldest months of the year in a state of apparent dormancy, living off stored deposits of fat and protein. It is worth noting that a temperature drop from 20 to 10°C will reduce protein digestibility, and since during autumn we are not trying to encourage growth, apart from it being wasteful and expensive to feed excessive levels of protein at this time, reduced digestibility can also lead to a bacterial overgrowth on protein left in the gut.

7.1.6 Immunity
As daylength shortens and temperatures fall, the koi immune system becomes less effective, and one may see the first signs of Carp Pox, or a reoccurrence of bacterial septicaemias and ulcers. These latter conditions should be attended to immediately.

7.1.7 Dormancy
During the winter, koi appear to enter a state of hibernation, characterised by reduced activity, a reduced response to external stimuli and a low respiration rate. It is not a true hibernation though, as the fish can still respond to stimuli, but their sluggish attempts to swim away in these circumstances may be more a reflection of their inability to react at these low temperatures, rather than a reduced perception of the stimulus. Breaking any ice that forms at the surface with a hammer is not a good idea, as shock waves will be sent through the water, where they will be sensed by the koi lateral line – a stress that may be too much in their weakened state. A floating heater is a much better way of keeping an area of pool surface clear.

Reduced metabolic rate means a sluggish circulation which, in the longer finned so-called Butterfly koi, may lead to congestion in the fins, predisposing them to damage and disease. At these very low temperatures, the immune system will be virtually ineffective. Fortunately, the majority of pathogens are also depressed by the low temperatures, so their ability to produce disease is reduced although, over a prolonged period of time, they may still build up to problem levels.

7.2.1 Spring

This is a particularly challenging time of year for koi in northern latitudes. Although many are produced in Japan, where the winters are colder than here in the UK, their winters are shorter and preceded by a longer and warmer summer, allowing more time for the fish to prepare for winter. In the wild, carp are inhabitants of large bodies of water, which allow a seasonal migration into deeper water during the winter months.

First of all, our summers are short, and so the koi must compress their spawning activities and build up for the winter into a maximum of only six months. Our winters are longer, stressing the fish, so that they may face spring in a very rundown condition. Koi produced or grown on in warmer climates, such as Israel or Singapore, may find their first winter particularly stressful.

Many koi are expected to subsist in totally inappropriate environments, often in ponds originally built for goldfish and which have an inadequate depth – two to two and a half feet seems to be the most popular, rather than the four-foot minimum recommended for koi.

Water quality may also be a problem, often due to high stocking levels. These high stocking densities also mean that even the most inefficient of pathogens will find it easy to spread to new fish. The UK spring can be a very unpredictable creature, with temperatures varying dramatically hour by hour on some days. Aside from stressing the koi, these temperature variations also affect the bacteria in the biological filters, again making water quality a potential problem.

All these factors cause the fish stress which, in turn, releases high levels of cortisol, producing a secondary suppression of the immune system. This situation is easily made worse by low environmental temperatures which slow down the immune response.

Appendices

Disease Flow Chart
an approach to a disease problem

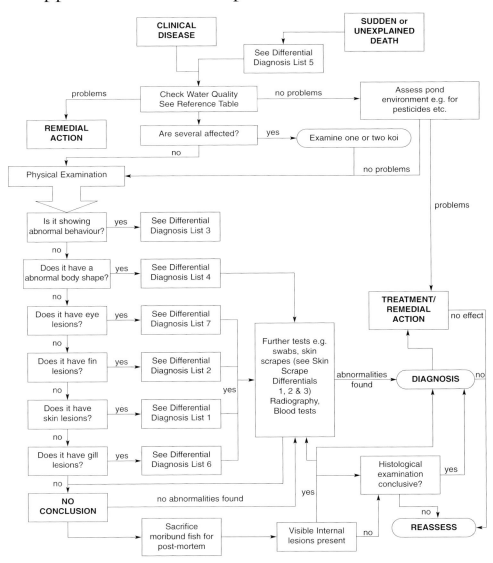

Differential Diagnoses

SKIN

Increased Mucus Production/Dulled/Altered Colouration

pH extremes	1.3.7;1.3.8
Ichthyobodo	5.7.4
Chilonodella	5.7.5
Trichodiniasis	5.7.8
Gyrodactylus	5.7.9
Oodinium	5.8.2

Gas Bubbles

Gas Bubble Disease	1.9.4

Erythema/Haemorrhages

High Chlorine	1.11.1
Spring Viraemia of Carp	5.3.4
Septicaemia	5.4.3
Aeromonas	5.4.6
Lactobacillus	5.4.9
Edwardsiella	5.4.10

Raised Scales

Chronic Bacterial Infection	6.4.3
Ascites (generalised)	5.4.3

Lumps/Masses

Carp Pox	5.3.3
Dermocystidium	5.6.4
Papillomatosis	6.3.3

Ulceration

Bacterial Ulcer Disease	5.4.3
Aeromonas	5.4.6
Cytophaga-like Bacteria	5.4.7
Columnaris	5.4.11
Corona-like virus	5.3.6
Mycobacteriosis	5.4.13
Trichodina	5.7.8
Sunburn	6.1.7
Trauma	6.1.10
Hypersensitivity Reactions	6.5.1

Visible Spots

Ichthyophithirius	5.7.6
Glocchidia	5.10.1

Fuzzy, Whitish Areas

Columnaris	5.4.11
Saprolegnia	5.6.2
Epistylis	5.7.7

Visible Parasites

Leeches	5.8.7
Argulus	5.9.2
Lernea	5.9.3

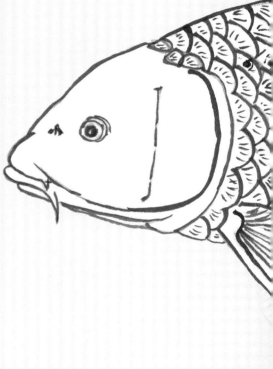

FINS

Erosion
High pH	1.3.8
Gas Bubble Disease	1.9.6
Cytophaga-like Bacteria	5.4.7
Columnaris	5.4.11

Haemorrhages
Septicaemia	5.4.3
Trauma	6.1.10

Lumps/Masses
Carp Pox	5.3.2
Papillomas	6.3.3

Clamped to Body
Septicaemia	5.4.3
Any Ectoparasitic Infestation	

Differential Diagnoses

BEHAVIORAL/MOVEMENT ABNORMALITIES

Increased Excitability
pH extremes	1.3.7; 1.4.8
High Ammonia (initially)	1.6.4
High Chlorine	1.11.0

Sluggishness
Low temperature	1.1.4
High Ammonia (long term)	1.6.4
Branchiomycosis	5.6.3
Trypanosoma	5.7.10

Scratching/Flicking
High Ammonia (initially)	1.6.4
Ectoparasites	

Swimming Disorders
Spring Viraemia of Carp	5.3.4
Septicaemias	5.4.3
Sphaerospora renicola	4.2.3; 5.7.11
Hoferellus cyprini	5.7.2
Myxosoma encephalina	5.7.11

BODY SHAPE

Swelling of Body Cavity
Spring Viraemia of Carp	5.4.3
Ascites	5.4.3
Bothriocephalus (in young koi)	5.8.2
Dystocia	6.2.2
Neoplasis	6.3.1

Spinal Curvature/Loss of Symmetry
Mycobacteriosis	5.4.13
Lightning Strike	6.1.4
Vitamin C Deficiency	6.2.5
Heavy Metal Toxicity	1.12.1
Pesticides	6.1.8
Neoplasia	6.3.1

Weight Loss/'Big Head'
Trypanoplasma	5.7.3
Eimeria	5.7.11
Tapeworms	5.8.4
Sekoke Disease	6.2.4
Neoplasia	6.3.1

SUDDEN/UNEXPECTED DEATH

Carbon Dioxide Toxicity (fish found dead in the morning)	1.10.4
Chlorine	1.11.1
Zinc Toxicity	1.12.1
Peracute Septicaemia	5.4.3
Lightning Strike/Electrical	6.1.4
Fatty Liver Disease	6.2.3

Differential Diagnoses

GILLS

Increased Respiratory Rate/ Respiratory Distress

Excessive high temperatures	1.1.4
High Ammonia	1.6.3
High Nitrite	1.7.3
Low Oxygen	1.9.4
High Chlorine	1.11.1
High Iron	1.12.1
Bacterial Gill Disease	5.4.8
Chilonodella	5.7.5
Ichthyophthirius	5.7.6
Trichodiniasis	5.7.8
Oodinium	5.7.9
Gyrodactylus	5.8.2
Dactylogyrus	5.8.3
Sanguinicola	5.8.5
Formalin Overdose	6.1.9
Malachite Green Overdose	6.1.9

Haemorrhages

Stress	5.2.2
Sanguinicola	5.8.5

Increased Mucus Production

Bacterial Gill Disease	5.4.8
Epitheliocystis	5.5.2
Ichthyobodo	5.7.4
Dactylogyrus	5.8.3

Gill Rot/Necrosis

Bacterial Gill Disease	5.4.8
Branchiomycosis	5.6.3

Gill Cysts

Epitheliocystis	5.5.2
Myxosoma dujardini	5.7.11
Henneguya koi	5.7.11

Visible Parasite

Ergasilus	5.9.4

Altered Colouration

Nitrite Toxicity (brown)	1.7.3
Trypanoplasma (pallor)	5.7.3
Trypanosoma (pallor)	5.7.10
Sphaerospora renicola (pallor)	4.2.3; 5.7.11

Operculum removed

Differential Diagnoses

OCULAR DISORDERS

Periocular/Retrobulbar

Gas Bubble Disease	1.9.4
Carp Pox	5.3.3
Erythrohoroma	6.3.2
Exophthalmos	6.4.2

Cornea

Erythrophoroma	6.3.2
Carp Pox	5.3.3
Keratitis	6.4.3
Papillomas	6.4.4

Lens

Diplostomum	5.8.7
Cataracts	6.4.5

Simplified Cross-
Section of a Koi Eye

Water Quality Normal Reference Ranges for Koi

Temperature	1.1.1	10 – 30°C (PBT 22-28°C)
pH	1.3.1	6.0 – 8.4 (preferred 7.5 – 8.0)
Hardness	1.4.1	100 – 250 mg/l CaCO3
Conductivity	1.4.3	180 – 480 mS/cm
Ammonia	1.6.1	< 0.02mg/l
Nitrite	1.7.1	<0.2mg/l
Nitrate	1.8.1	<40mg/l above ambient tapwater levels
Oxygen	1.9.4	5.0 - 8.0 mg/l
Redox Potential	1.9.2	pe = 27-32
Chlorine	1.11.1	<0.002mg/l

External Anatomy

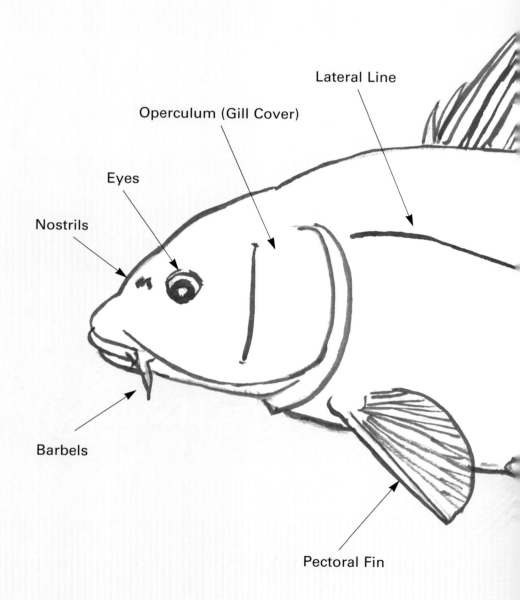

Lateral Line

Operculum (Gill Cover)

Eyes

Nostrils

Barbels

Pectoral Fin

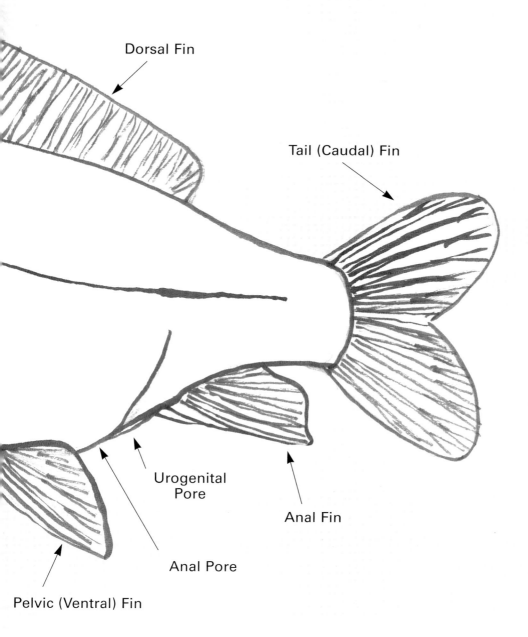

Dorsal Fin

Tail (Caudal) Fin

Urogenital
Pore

Anal Fin

Anal Pore

Pelvic (Ventral) Fin

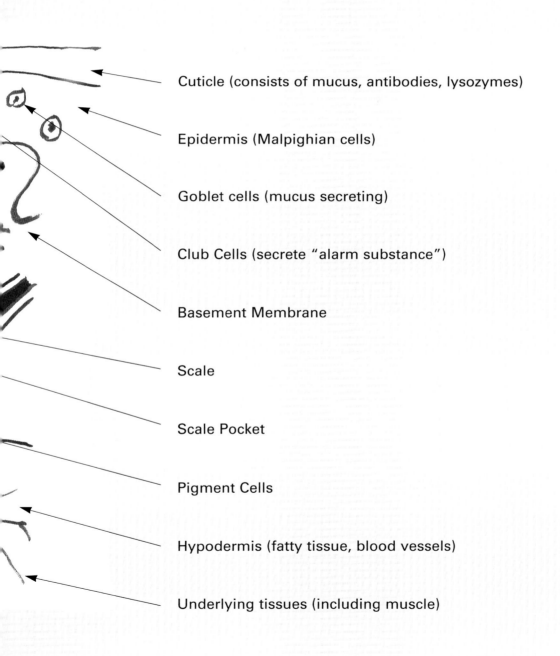

Cuticle (consists of mucus, antibodies, lysozymes)

Epidermis (Malpighian cells)

Goblet cells (mucus secreting)

Club Cells (secrete "alarm substance")

Basement Membrane

Scale

Scale Pocket

Pigment Cells

Hypodermis (fatty tissue, blood vessels)

Underlying tissues (including muscle)

Skin Scrape Differential 1

Ichthyobodo
10-20 μm

Chilonodella
50-70 μm

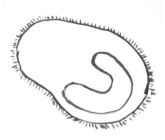

Ichthyophthirius
0.5-1.0 mm

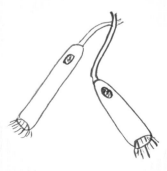

Epistylis
50-100 μm

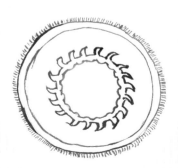

Trichodina
50-60 μm

Skin Scrape Differential 2

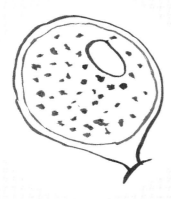

Oodinium
40-100 µm

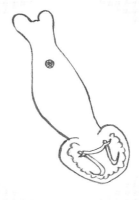

Gyrodactylus
0.3-0.5 mm

Dactylogyrus
0.3-0.5 mm

Leech
(Piscicola)
< 4.0 cm

Skin Scrape Differential 3

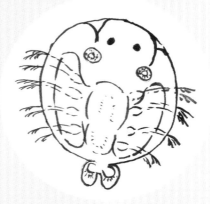

Argulus
L <7 mm

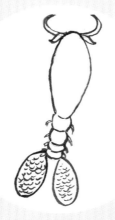

Ergasilus
L 1.5 mm

Learna
L 20 mm

Further Reading

For veterinary surgeons, and those requiring more information on fish diseases and their treatment, I would recommend the following:

Bacterial Diseases of Fish
Inglis, Roberts and Bromage (Eds) 1993
Blackwell Scientific Publications, Osney Mead, Oxford, OX2 0EL
ISBN 0-632-03497-1

Colorguide of Tropical Fish Diseases
Basslear G. 1983 Basslear Biofish, Stationstraat 130, B-2235 Westmeerbeek, Belgium
ISBN 90-03-98085-3

Fish Medicine
Stoskopf, Michael K. 1993 W.B.Saunders Company, Harcourt Brace and Company, The Curtis Center, Independence Square West, Philadelphia, Pennsylvania 19106
ISBN 0-7216-2629-7

Self-Assessment Colour Review of Ornamental Fish
Lewbart G.A. 1998 Manson Publishing Ltd, 73 Corringham Road, London, NW11 7DL
ISBN 1-874545-81-2

Textbook of Fish Health (Revised and Expanded)
Post G. 1987 T.F.H. Publications Inc, 211 West Sylvania Avenue, Neptune City, NJ 07753
ISBN 0-86622-491-2

The Interpet Manual of Fish Health
Andrews, Excell and Carrington 1988
Salamander Books Ltd, 52 Bedford Row, London, WC1R 4LR
ISBN 0-86101-368-9

The Veterinary Formulary (Fourth Edition)
Bishop, Y. (Ed) 1998 Pharmaceutical Press, 1 Lambeth High Street, London, SE1 7JN
ISBN 0-85369-412-5

Veterinary Clinics of North America, Exotic Animal Practice series
W.B.Saunders Company, Harcourt Brace and Company, The Curtis Center, Independence Square West, Philadelphia, Pennsylvania 19106
ISSN 1094-9194
These cover fish medicine as well as amphibians, reptiles, birds and small mammals.

Journal of Fish Diseases
Blackwell Scientific Publications, Osney Mead, Oxford, OX2 0EL
ISSN 0140-7775

The Interpet Encyclopedia of Koi
McDowall A. (Ed) 1989 Salamander Books Ltd, 52 Bedford Row, London, WC1R 4LR
ISBN 0-86101-405-7
An excellent introductory book on care and the hobby side of koi keeping.

Veterinary surgeons wanting to pursue their interest in fish disease should consider contacting the following organisations:

British Veterinary Zoological Society (BVZS)
c/o 7 Mansfield Street, London W1M 0AT, UK

Fish Veterinary Society
Contact Fiona Macdonald BVMS MRCVS
Pinckneys Farm, Marten, Marlborough, Wiltshire, SN8 3SJ or via email
fiona.macdonald@btinternet.com

Useful Addresses

LABORATORY SERVICES

Laboratories that I have found useful and are experienced in dealing with fish related samples are:

FINN Pathologists
One Eyed Lane
Weybread
Diss
Norfolk
IP21 5TT UK (Histopathology only)

Greendale Laboratories Ltd.
Lansbury Estate
Lower Guildford Road
Knaphill
Woking
Surrey
GU21 2BR UK

IDEXX Laboratories
Grange House
P.O. Box 4
Wetherby
West Yorkshire
LS22 4ZR UK

Institute of Aquaculture
University of Stirling
FK9 4LA UK

OTHER USEFUL ORGANISATIONS

Those wishing to find out more about the hobby of koi keeping should contact:

British Koi Keepers Society (B.K.K.S.)
via their website www.bkks.co.uk

Ornamental Aquatics Trade Association
(OATA) Ltd
Contact:
Keith Davenport
The Chief Executive
Ornamental Aquatic Trade Association
(OATA) Ltd.
Unit 5
Narrow Wine Street
Trowbridge
Wiltshire
BA14 8YY UK
Website www.ornamentalfish.org/

Ornamental Fish International (OFI)
OFI Secretariat
Apartado de Correos No. 129
29692 - Sabinillas
Manilva
Málaga
Spain
Website www.ornamental-fish-int.org/

These are addresses of services and organisations that I have found useful in my own work. I'm sure that you will find similar facilities in your own location or country.

Notes & Useful Addresses

Index